WARSHIP MONOGRAPHS
INVINCIBLE CLASS

WARSHIP MONOGRAPHS

INVINCIBLE CLASS

John A. Roberts

CONWAY MARITIME PRESS
1972

7 Nelson Road, Greenwich, London, S.E.10.

ISBN 0 85177 051 7

Printed in Great Britain by
Latimer Trend & Co. Ltd.
Whitstable Kent

Contents

Acknowledgements

My thanks are due to Mr. A. Preston for his valuable assistance in the production of this work. Also to Mr. A. Raven for help with the section on colour schemes and to the National Maritime Museum for permission to study the Ships Covers.

JOHN A. ROBERTS

Illustrations and Plans

Introduction

Since the latter part of the 19th century the duties of cruisers, although many and varied, have been reasonably well defined. The design of the ships themselves, however, has been in a constant state of flux depending upon the naval policy of the period and until 1914, the policy on cruiser design was seriously hampered by lack of war experience

By the 1890s cruisers had developed into 1st, 2nd and 3rd class protected cruisers, designed for commerce protection. In 1899 the armoured cruiser was reintroduced and from this type the battlecruiser was evolved. At much the same time the smaller cruisers developed into the *Town* classes and the light cruisers of the *Arethusa* class. In 1914 all the old protected cruisers and the armoured cruisers were obsolete, leaving two basic types, the battlecruiser and the light cruiser, to be tested in action.

H.M.S. Indomitable in reserve at Sheerness in 1919.

THE RE-INTRODUCTION OF THE ARMOURED CRUISER 1899 – 1905

The 5,600 ton *Orlando* class armoured cruisers of 1886 carried an armament of two 9.2 in. and ten 6 in. guns mounted on a hull protected by a 10 in. armour belt and a 2 in. deck. The class proved to be very unsatisfactory, their speed of 18 knots being insufficient for cruiser duties, and their shallow armour belt, barely showing above the water line, was virtually useless. However, an armoured vessel possessing the necessary speed and range for cruiser operations could only have been constructed on what, in the 1880s, would have been considered an excessively large displacement. Therefore the construction of armoured cruisers lapsed for some years and only protected cruisers were built for the Royal Navy. The 1st class protected cruiser however, steadily increased in size and reached its peak with the 14,200 ton *Powerful* and *Terrible* in 1895.

The development of cemented armour plate in the 1890s, which provided a considerable saving in weight over compound armour and improvements in machinery design had by the end of the century made the construction of armoured cruisers a reasonable proposition once again, and urged on by events abroad, the Admiralty recommenced armoured cruiser construction in 1899 with the *Cressy* class. Table 1 gives the main particulars of the armoured cruisers built for the Royal Navy during the period 1899 – 1905.

The *Cressy* class were virtually 1st class protected cruisers with a belt; *Drake* class were much the same but with increased speed and consequently larger displacement. The "County" class were built specifically to counter foreign cruisers designed for commerce and the *Devonshires* were improved versions. The last three classes were designed mainly for fleet work with an eye on German naval expansion rather than French commerce raiders. As can be seen, although speed and armour protection was fairly uniform through the classes the armament steadily increased in size. In the *Cressy* class all but the two 9.2 in. guns were mounted in casemates. The value of guns thus mounted is limited and during the armoured cruisers short period of development the casemate gradually gave way to the turret mounting, the *Warrior* and *Minotaur* classes carrying turrets only.

DEVELOPMENT OF A NEW CONCEPT

In 1902, Admiral Fisher with the help of Constructor W.H. Gard, began to formulate the details of an armoured cruiser which would make all existing vessels of this type obsolete in much the same way as the *Dreadnought* was to make all existing battleships obsolete. As finally worked out this vessel was to be armed with four 9.2 in. guns mounted in two turrets (originally the main armament was 10 in., but the

Class	Displacement	Armament	Speed	Belt Armour
CRESSY 1899	12,000 tons	2 – 9.2" 12 – 6"	21.5 knots	6"
DRAKE 1900	14,100 tons	2 – 9.2" 16 – 6"	24 knots	6"
"COUNTY" CLASS 1901	9,800 tons	14 – 6"	23.5 knots	4"
DEVONSHIRE 1902	10,850 tons	4 – 7.5" 6 – 6"	22 knots	6"
DUKE OF EDINBURGH 1903	12,590 tons	6 – 9.2" 10 – 6"	22.5 knots	6"
WARRIOR 1904	13,350 tons	6 – 9.2" 4 – 7.5"	23 knots	6"
MINOTAUR 1905	14,600 tons	4 – 9.2" 10 – 7.5"	23 knots	6"

Table 1

9.2 in. was considered more efficient on a weight for weight basis) and twelve 7.5 in. mounted in six turrets. She was to have a speed of 25 knots, superior to any existing armoured cruiser, powered by turbine machinery of 35,000 horse power and oil fired boilers. The armour on the belt, bulkheads and 9.2 in. turrets was 6in. thick, on the 7.5 in. turrets it was 4 in. thick and on the decks 3 in. to 1½ in. thick. The displacement was 14,000 tons (15,000 tons if coal-fired) and the minimum length (pp) 500 feet. In addition Fisher had a strong desire to reduce the top hamper by the use of, among other things, telescopic funnels and light bridges and by fitting no masts except for a light pole for wireless.

The Admiralty's answer to the Fisher/Gard cruiser was the *Minotaur* class, which did not really meet the requirements put forward by Fisher, being virtually conventional armoured cruisers, lacking most of all, the 25 knots speed which Fisher had begun to regard as all important.

Fisher's conception of a new armoured cruiser was further influenced by events abroad, mainly from the Russo-Japanese war in which, during the battle of Tsu-Shima the Japanese superiority in speed played a major part in the defeat of the Russian fleet. There was also evidence of similar lines of thought among foreign navies. In 1904 the Japanese laid down the *Ikoma* and *Tsukuba* of 13,750 tons armed with four 12 in. and twelve six in. guns, protected by a 7 in. belt and with a speed of 20.5 knots and the Italians the *Regina Elena* of 12,500 tons armed with two 12 in. and twelve 8 in. guns, protected by a 10"/8" belt and with a speed of 22 knots. Both these designs inclined towards the fast battleship rather than the heavily armed, high speed armoured cruiser that Fisher envisaged.

THE COMMITTEE ON DESIGNS

When Fisher became 1st Sea Lord in October 1904, one of his first actions was to place his designs before the Cabinet, with the intention of forming a committee on new designs responsible for working out the details of his new ships. The members of the committee were chosen in December 1904 and included the Director of Naval Construction Phillip Watts, R. Froude, W. Gard, Sir John Thornycroft, Prince Louis of Battenberg, Admirals Bacon, Jackson, Jellicoe and others. The committee thus contained men of high reputation and considerable knowledge of all aspects of warship design and operation, whose combined opinions could hardly be ignored. The committee was, therefore, an ideal instrument with which Fisher, as chairman, could push through his revolutionary ideas without concentrating upon himself all the criticism that would undoubtedly follow such a radical departure from existing warship design.

The Committee was officially appointed on the 22nd December 1904 and first met on the 3rd January 1905. Initially they were preoccupied with the new battleship *Dreadnought*, the design of which was finalised on the 13th January. The original specification for the new armoured cruisers which the committee was to consider was very open. The new ships were to carry 12 in. guns, have armour to the same standard as the *Minotaur* class and a speed of 25 knots, and be designed with consideration of existing docking facilities. Five sketch designs were placed before the committee on the 12th January 1905. The first (Design A) a product of Fisher and Gard, the rest from the Constructors' department.

The committee preferred design E, but asked for an alternative design (F) to be worked out on the lines of design A but with the forward turrets placed further aft and with the two after turrets further apart on the upper deck, one well aft and the other between the engine and boiler rooms, if necessary. Presumably they did not like the superfiring turret aft due to the possibility of blast effect and considered that the forward turrets might be wet.

The committee met again on the 13th and decided not to proceed with design F. Design E was recommended as far as the disposition and number of 12 in. guns was concerned. They therefore asked for design E with turbine machinery, which would provide a saving in weight, to be more fully worked out, with more detailed information concerning the displacement, machinery arrangement, etc. This more detailed legend was placed before the committee on 21st Jan. 1905.

The committee made some alterations to this legend, including the reduction of the speed to 25 knots with 41,000 S.H.P., and then presented it to the Board for approval. On the 20th March 1905 the Board adopted the outline design submitted by the committee and the details were passed on to the Constructors Department. Constructor J.H. Narbeth was entrusted with the work of completing the design of the three new armoured cruisers, which were to be included in the estimates for 1905/6.

The beam had been reduced to 78 ft. 6 ins. as a result of calculations, and it was found necessary to increase the displacement to 17,250 tons to provide sufficient weight for the machinery, including 70 tons for oil fuel and fittings, and the Board margin of 100 tons. In addition to these alterations two of the forward boiler uptakes were combined thus reducing the number of funnels to three.

All three ships were laid down in 1906, the *Inflexible* on 5 Feb. at Clydebank, the *Indomitable* on 1 Mar. at Fairfields and the *Invincible* on 2 April at Elswick. (In the Ships' Cover the names of the three ships for 1905 are given as *Invincible, Immortalite* and *Raleigh).*

MODIFICATIONS DURING CONSTRUCTION

The most important alteration to the design while the ships were under construction was the substitution of sixteen 4 in. for the twenty 12-pounders in the original design. The following information is con-

Design	A	B	C	D & E
Displacement	17,000 tons	17,200 tons	16,600 tons	17,750 tons
Length (ft)	540	540	520	550
Beam (ft)	77	77.5	76	79
Draught (ft)	26.5	26.5	26	26.6
Speed (knots)	25.5	25.5	25	25.5
Armament	8 – 12″	8 –12″	6 – 12″	8 – 12″
	13 – 4″	13 – 4″		13 – 4″

All the above designs were for reciprocating machinery.

LEGEND

Displacement	16,850 tons
Dimensions	540′ x 79′ x 26′
S.H.P.	42,500 = 25.5 knots
Coal	1000 tons at load draught
Armament	8 – 12″, 14 – 4″
	2 – maxims, 5 submerged torpedo tubes
Armour	Belt 6″ & 4″, bulkheads 6″ barbettes 8″, turrets 8″, splinter protection 2″, C.T. 10″ & 6″, communication tube 6″ & 2″, Lower deck 2″ & 1½″

Weights	
General equipment	620 tons
Armament	2500 tons
Machinery	3140 tons
Coal	1000 tons
Armour & backing	3370 tons
Hull	6120 tons
	16750 tons
Board margin	100 tons
	16850 tons

The above details were worked out on the basis that the use of turbines would give a 12½% saving in machinery weight. A second legend was also produced assuming a 30% saving! The details were the same as those above except for the following:— Displacement 15,700 tons, length 525 ft., Machinery 2,350 tons, armour & backing 3,300 tons Hull 5,850 tons.

Indomitable at Chatham 1910.

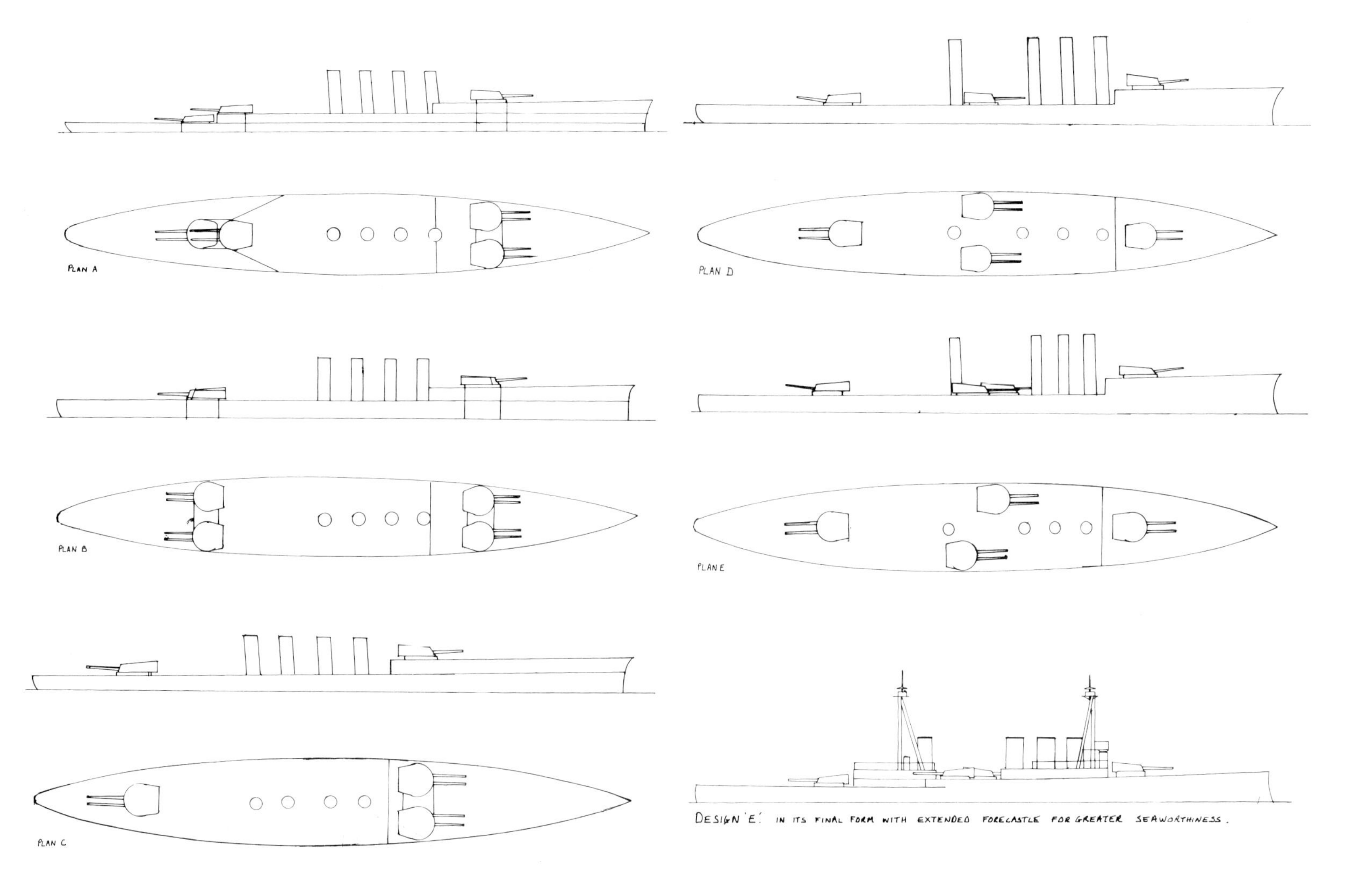

DESIGN 'E'. IN ITS FINAL FORM WITH EXTENDED FORECASTLE FOR GREATER SEAWORTHINESS.

tained in the Ships' Cover relating to additions to thc design up to May 1907. The increase of 70 tons added about 1 in. to the draught. In addition to this weight *Invincible* had to carry another 130 tons due to her electrically operated turrets (see armament section) and in all three ships a weight of 80 tons was added to provide balancing for the 12 in. guns. This resulted in a total additional weight of 150 tons (280 tons in *Invincible*) on the legend displacement.

ARMAMENT

The main armament of the *Invincible* was so disposed as to give an all round fire of six 12 in. guns. The midships turrets were mounted en-echelon so that, in the event of one of the wing turrets being disabled, rhe other could fire across the opposite beam. This was not possible while both turrets were manned due to blast effects. This was, however a very limited advantage as the arc of fire available in this situation was only 30°. The ahead and astern fire, although designed for six guns, was effectively only four guns. First, the target had to be dead ahead or astern and second, even supposing this ideal situation to exist, the blast effects on the superstructure were considerable. The design might well have been improved by dropping the two wing turrets altogether and mounting a single turret amidships on the centre line. This would have kept the broadside at six 12 in. guns but reduced the effective ahead and astern fire by 50%. The latter was a debatable disadvantage considering that the weight saved could have been utilised for additional armour protection without any loss in speed.

As a result of confusion experienced in the *Dreadnought* the designation of the wing turrets in the *Invincibles* was altered from B and C to P and Q on 30 Oct. 1906.

The secondary armament disposed in the fore and aft superstructures and on the turret roofs was designed for use against torpedo boats and destroyers. During construction the original requirement for 20 pdr. 18 cwt. guns was latered to sixteen of the new 4 in. MK III Q.F's with a range of 9000 yds and firing a 25 lbs. shell.

12 in. ELECTRIC MOUNTING

On the 21 Mar. 1905 a conference was held at the Admiralty to consider a design by the Elswick Ordnance Company for electrically powered turrets. Six months later, in Aug. 1905, the Board approved a proposal that one of the *Invincible* class should be fitted with electrically worked turrets. However, in order to complete the designs as quickly as possible tenders for the ships were to be asked for on the assumption that all three vessels would have hydraulically powered turrets, the necessary modifications being made at a later date.

Two tenders for electric turrets were accepted by the Admiralty, presumably so that both designs might be fully evaluated.

Design Work

The sheer drawing, midship section, armour and rig drawings, the legend and weight calculations were completed on the 22nd June 1905. The design generally conformed to that put forward by the committee:—

LEGEND — 22 June 1905

Displacement	17,250 tons (19,720 tons deep load)
Dimensions	530′ x 78′6″ x 26′
S.H.P.	41,000 = 25 knots
Coal	1000 tons (at load draught)
Armament	8 — 12″, 24* — 12 pdr. — 2 Maxims, 5 submerged torpedo tubes.
Armour	Belt 6″ & 4″; bulkheads 7″ & 6″; barbettes 7″; turrets 7″; C.T. 10″ & 6″; communication tube 4″ & 3″; Upper deck (over magazines) 2½″; main deck (forward) ¾″, (under forward & midships barbettes and crowns of lower C.T.'s) 1″; Lower deck (on flats) 1½″ forward and amidships 2½″ aft; (on slopes 1½″ 1½″ forward, 2″ midships, 2½″ aft.

* Later reduced to 20 — 12 pdr.

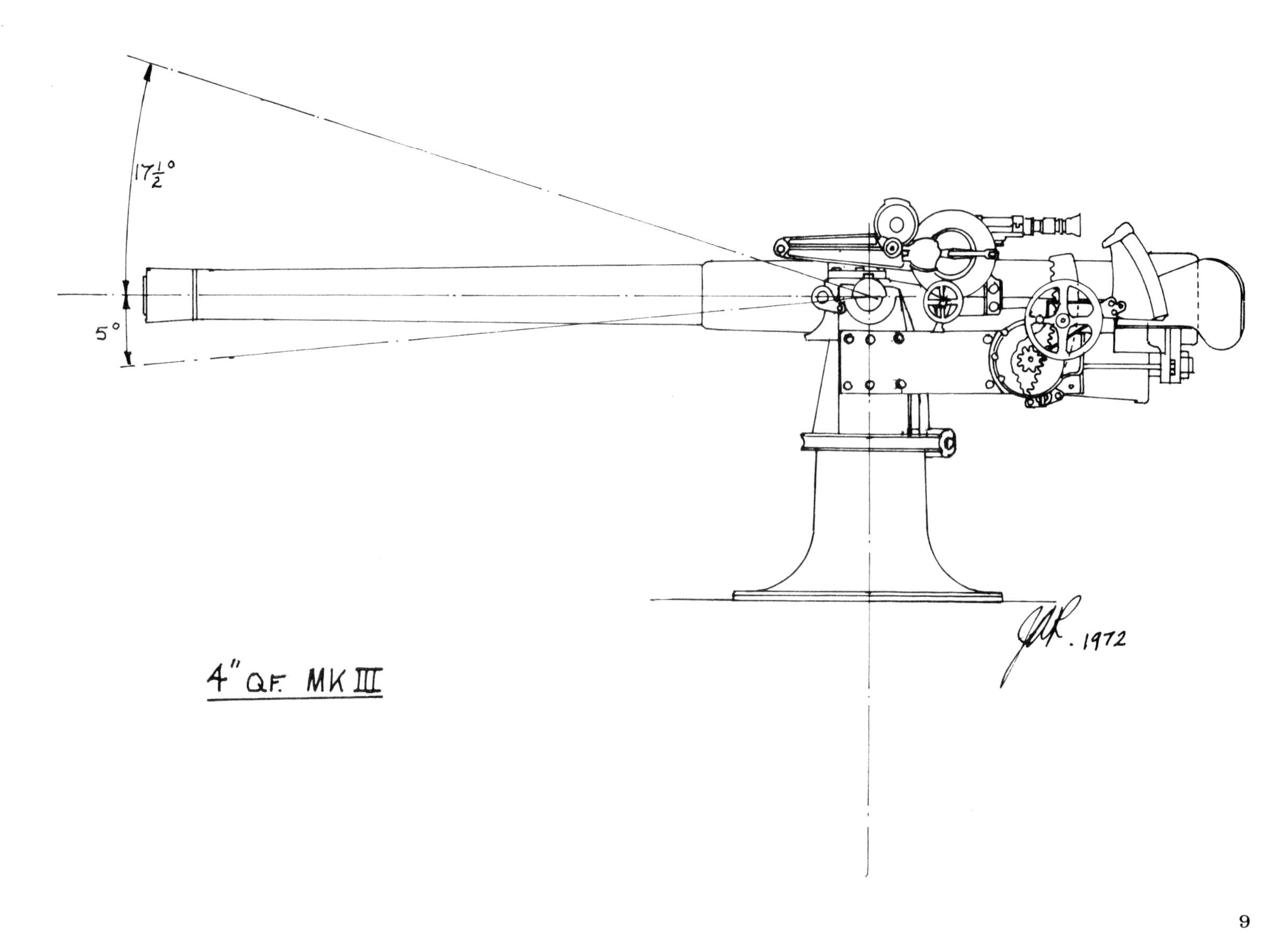

4" Q.F. MK III

Alteration	Added Weight (tons)
Already appropriated up to 1907	10
Replacing 20–12 pdr. with 16–4″	65
Addition of 14″ torpedoes, stores and dropping gear for 50′ boats.	5
Addition of fitting to keep cable lockers clean	5
Addition of fittings for separate saluting magazine	2
Fitting armament office, messes for domestics	3
Substitution of cases for airtight lockers in magazine	40
Increase in height of mast to 180′ above L.W.L.	5
Additional magazine cooling arrangements	30
Addition of air blast for 12″ guns	5
Total	170
Board Margin	100
Legend Displacement exceeded by	70

One was from Armstrongs, at 345 tons per turret (without guns) and the other from Vickers at 365 tons per turret, (without guns). *Invincible* herself was chosen as the test ship Armstrongs providing P and Q turrets and Vickers A and Y turrets.

All three ships carried out their gun trials off the Isle of Wight in 1908. The *Indomitable* on 23 Apr., the *Inflexible* on 18 June and the *Invincible* on 30 Oct. In all cases the results were satisfactory except that the electric training and elevating gear in the *Invincible* was found to be too slow. Various further trials were made with the electric gear but it soon became evident that "the design of the electric appliances for working the turrets etc., in this vessel *(Invincible)* are faulty and it is improbable that they would ever be made to work satisfactory without redesign and replacement"*. On 20 Mar. 1912 a conference was held at the Admiralty on the conversion of *Invincible's* turrets to hydraulic power. The D.N.O. estimated that it would take 6 months and about £151,000 to carry out the conversion which was scheduled to take place during Oct. 1912 until May 1913. In actual fact the conversion was not made until *Invincible's* long refit of 1914.

Of the three different types of 12 in. mountings employed in the class the BVIII was the hydraulically operated version fitted in the *Indomitable* and *Inflexible.* The BIX and BX were the electrically operated mountings fitted in *Invincible,* the former being the Vickers mounting (A & Y turrets) and the latter the Armstrong mounting (P & Q turrets). In all three the turrets were of different shape and this point is well illustrated in the drawing of the *Invincible* where it can be seen that the wing and end turrets are of different design.

* *Ships Cover*

MACHINERY

The *Invincible* class were driven by ten Parsons turbines, four ahead (two low and two high pressure) four astern (two low pressure and two high pressure) and two cruising turbines (high pressure). The cruising turbines were fitted one on each high pressure turbine shaft for low cruising speeds. The high pressure turbines were attached to the outer shafts and the low pressure to the inner shafts. At full power the steam was passed through the high pressure turbine into the low pressure turbine and then through the condenser. At lower powers steam went through the cruising turbine first, then via the high and low pressure turbines to the condenser; when going astern through the high and low pressure reverse turbines to the condenser. All four screws were three-bladed, the inner screws being 10 ft. 6 ins. and the outer screws 9 ft 6 ins in diameter, with a pitch of 11 ft 4 ins (except in *Invincible* with a 10 ft 11 in. pitch.) The *Invincible's* turbines were built by Humphreys of Tennant and the others by the builders.

Ballistics

	12″ Mk X B.L.	4″ Mk III Q.F.
Construction	Wire	Wire
Weight of gun, without breech mechanism	56 tons 16 cwt	1 ton 6 cwt
Total length of gun	558″	165.25″
Length of bore, including chamber	540″ (45 cal)	160″ (40 cal)
Weight of shell	850 lbs	25 lbs
Weight of charge	258 lbs	3 lbs 9 ozs
Nature of charge	M.D. Cordite	M.D.T. or Mk1 Cordite
Muzzle velocity	2,725 f.s.	2,300 f.s.
Muzzle energy	47,800 ft.	917 ft.
Maximum rate of fire	2 rpm.	20 rpm.
Penetration of wrought iron at muzzle	51″	12.4″
Penetration of wrought iron at 3000 yards	38″	5″
Penetration of Krupp steel at 3000 yards	17″	
Shell Complement		
Rounds per gun	80	100
Made up as follows:—		
A.P.C. (Armour piercing capped)	192	—
Steel common	320	800
Lyddite common	128	800
Total	640	1600
Practice	24	224
Full charges	640	18024
Mountings	BVIII B1X BX	P1
Weight of one mounting excluding guns (tons)	335 371 347	

The *Invincible* and *Inflexible* were fitted with 31 Yarrow boilers and the *Indomitable* with 31 Babcock and Wilcox boilers. They were arranged in four boiler rooms, with seven boilers in No. 1 boiler room and eight in the others. The magazines and shellrooms for P and Q turrets were between boiler rooms 3 and 4. The working pressure was 250 lbs. per square inch.

All the boilers were supplemented with oil fuel burners which increased the range by about 700 nautical miles at full speed. The *Invincible* was fitted with five burners per boiler with a consumption of 180 lbs/hour/burner, the *Indomitable* with four burners at 240 lbs./hour/burner and the *Inflexible* with three burners at 300 lbs/hour/burner, the variation presumably being to test the different systems. The oil fuel carried was 700 tons with 3,000 tons of coal at deep load and 1,000 tons at load draught.

The machinery was probably the most successful aspect of the *Invincible* class design. Showing, as the *Dreadnought* had done, their superiority over reciprocating machinery, turbines also had the ability to maintain high speeds over a long period without problems (an almost impossible task with steam piston engines). *Indomitable* made a record average speed of 25.3 knots with 43,700 SHP, for three days, between Belleisle and Fasnet on her return journey from Canada in Aug. 1908. The class also showed a remarkably low fuel consumption

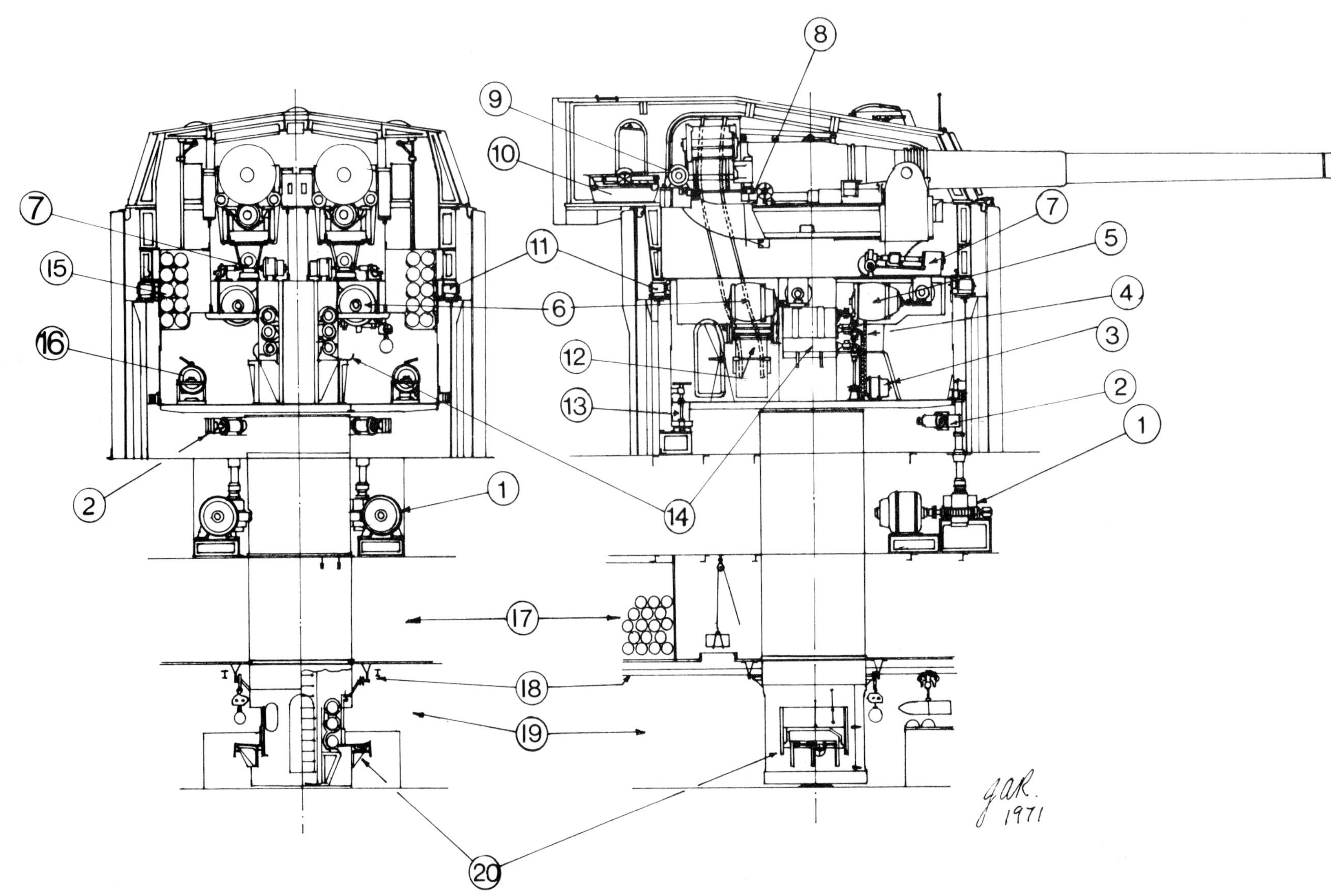

1
2
3
4
5
6
7
8
9
10
11
12
13
14
15
16
17
18
19
20
JAR
1971

PROPOSED DESIGN BY THE E.O.C., FOR THE INVINCIBLE'S ELECTRICALLY OPERATED TURRETS.

1. Electric training gear
2. Training stop
3. Gear for working rammers
4. Rammers
5. Motor for central hoist
6. Motor for main hoist
7. Elevating gear
8. Hand and electrically operated Breech mechanism
9. Chain rammer
10. Hand loading tray
11. Turret rollers and roller path
12. Loading cage
13. Spring locking bolt
14. Folding tray
15. Shell stowage
16. Winch
17. Magazine
18. Overhead rail
19. Shell room
20. Loading tray

STEERING TRIALS

The *Indomitable* carried out her steering trials on 30 Apr. 1908 and *Inflexible* on 27 Jun. the same year. The following are the results of *Invincible's* turning, steering engine and reversing trials which took place in Nov. 1908.

Reversing trial – with ship travelling ahead, all boilers alight and engines at 275 revs.

Inflexible docked at Gibraltar in 1915 after being mined.▷

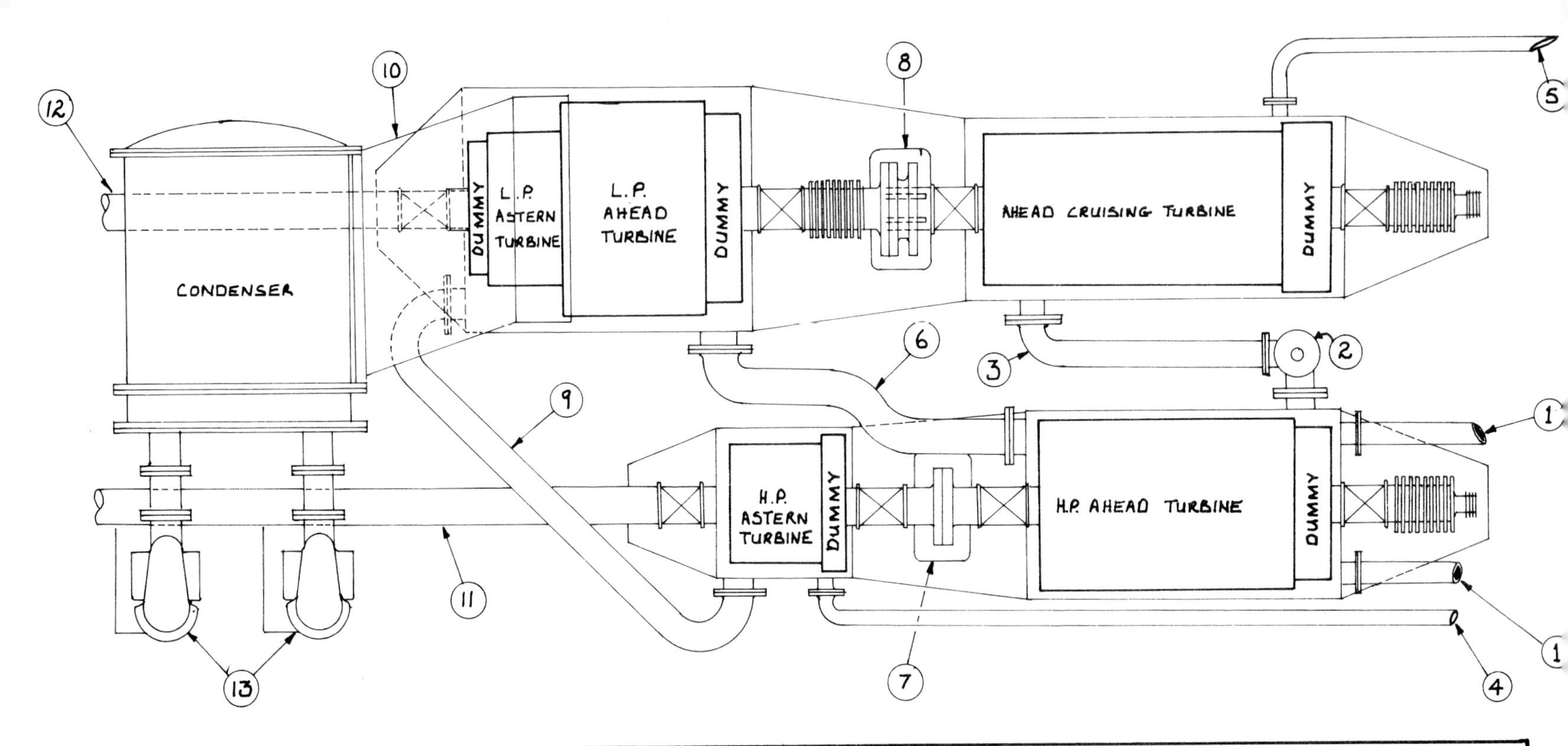

The differences in the weight of the boilers and water were much greater than anticipated in the original design, showing a 151 tons difference between the Yarrow and Babcock – 10% in favour of Yarrow.

Machinery Weights		INFLEXIBLE (Yarrow Boilers)	INDOMITABLE (Babcock Boilers)
Main engines		1,326.3 tons	1,295.4 tons
Shafts & propellors		141.9	140.7
Boilers		1,277.5	1,461.0
Water in boilers		159.6	127.0
Water in condensers		66.1	58.5
Feed tanks (approx)		25	25
Aux. Mach.	(Evaporators	40.2	42.8
	(Steering	13.8	15.7
		3,047.4 tons	3,166.1 tons

DIAGRAMATIC ARRANGEMENT OF STARBOARD ENGINE ROOM

1. Main steam pipes from boilers to H.P. turbine
2. Non return valve
3. Exhaust from cruising turbine to H.P. turbine.
4. Main steam pipes from boilers H.P. to astern turbine
5. Main steam pipe to cruising turbine
6. Exhaust from H.P. to L.P. turbine
7. Fixed coupling
8. Sliding coupling
9. Exhaust from H.P. to L.P. astern turbine.
10. Exhaust to condenser
11. Outer shaft
12. Inner shaft
13. Centrifugal pumps

Time from order being given to ship stopping – 3 min. 25 sec.
Distance travelled in this time 1,592 yards. Time from ship stopping to full astern 3 min. 48 secs. Distance travelled in this time 570 yards.

The *Invincible* steamed full astern for two minutes and reached a speed of 15.5 knots. The *Invincibles* like the *Dreadnought* were equipped with twin balanced rudders positioned immediately abaft the two inner screws. The rudder area was thus made relatively large and excellent manouvering ability resulted, the tactical diameter being much reduced compared with previous vessels.

Steam trials

The following details of the trials of the three ships are taken from the Ship's Cover:–

INDOMITABLE

Trial	1/5 power	7/10 power	7/10 power	full power
Date	22/4/08	26/4/08	27/4/08	29/4/08
Place	Skelmorlie	Polperro	Skelmorlie	Skelmorlie
No. of runs	4	6	6	4
Draught–Forward	25′1″	25′8″	25′1″	25′
Draught–Aft	26′3″	26′10″	26′3″	27′
Displacement	17,120 tons	17,620 tons	17,120 tons	17,435 tons
Speed	16.5 knots	22.488 knots	23.665 knots	26.106 knots
SHP–Inner (stb)	1,908	5,777	7,553	10,681
SHP–Outer (stb)	2,734	8,501	8,680	12,429
SHP–Inner (pt)	2,339	5,427	6,791	11,705
SHP–Outer (pt)	3,323	7,035	7,954	12,976
Total SHP	11,304	26,740	30,978	47,791
RPM–Inner (stb)	167	232	250	277
RPM–Outer (stb)	187	271	277	307
RPM–Inner (pt)	173	229	243	285
RPM–Outer(pt)	185	260	272	316
Mean RPM	178	248	260	296

In addition to the above, two long distance high power runs were made in opposite directions, between Pladda and Ailsa Craig, a distance of 10.48 miles, with the following results:–

SHP	44,220
RPM	288
Coal consumption	1.24 lbs/HP/Hour
EHP	22,450
Propeller co-efficient	50.77

Longitudinal section of H.M.S. *Invincible* as completed. Note the very large engine room compartment, divided by a centre line bulkhead into port and starboard engine rooms. When *Invincible's* turrets were converted to hydraulic power the motor generators for A and Y turrets in compartments 18 and 74, respectively, were removed. The upper dynamo room (45) was taken out and replaced by an athwartships hydraulic engine room, (44), against the after bulkhead. The 12" magazines for P and Q turrets being joined across the ship in the foreward half of the compartment.

1. Water tight compartment
2. Carpenter's store
3. Spirit room
4. Medical room
5. Canvas room
6. Boatswains store
7. W.O.'s washplace
8. Chain locker
9. Store
10. Capstan engine room.
11. Provision room
12 Boatswains store
13. Cabin
14. Marines slops
15. Lobby
16. Paymaster's slops
17. Dynamo room
18. Motor generator compartment

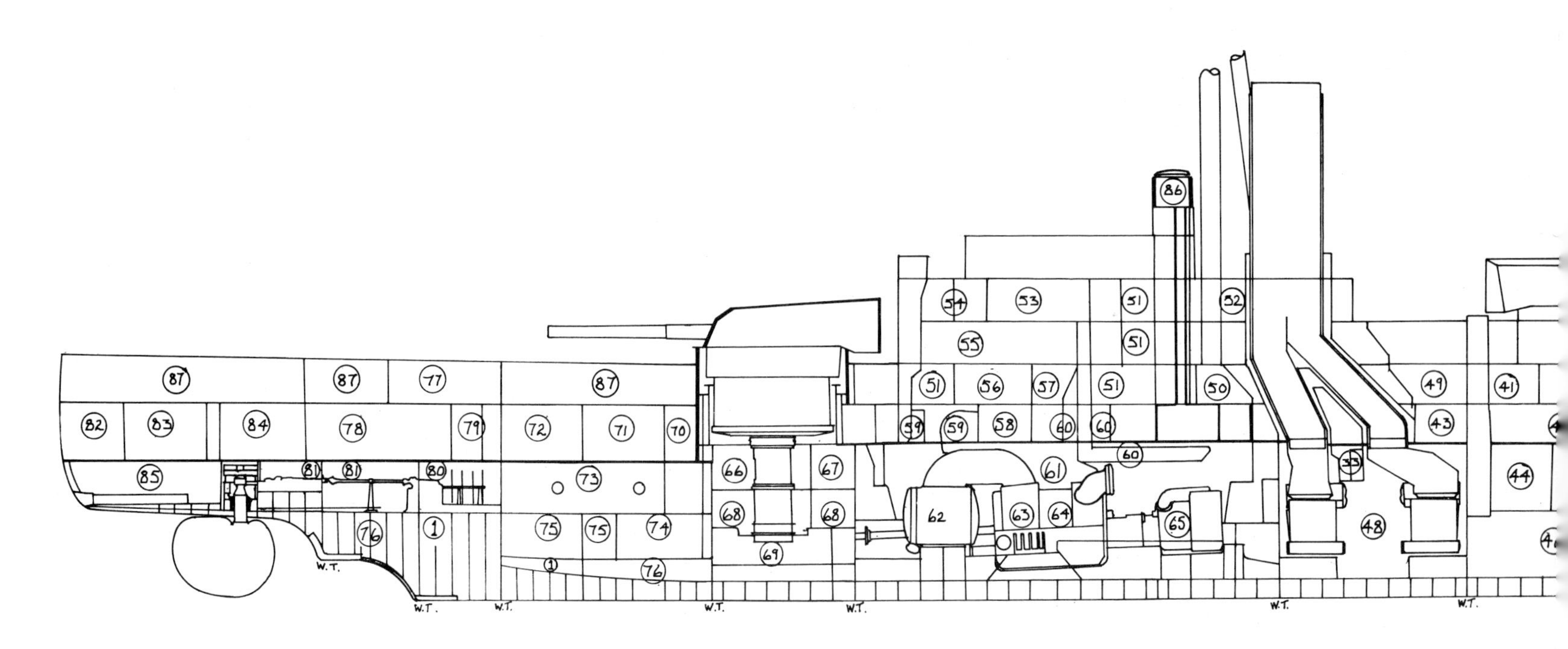

19. Store
20. Midshipman's study
21. Refrigerating machinery and torpedo store
22. Submerged torpedo room
23. Magazine
24. Searchlight store
25. Shell room
26. Gunners stores
27. Telephone exchange
28. Handing room
29. Drain tank
30. Admiral's day cabin (port), Admiral's dining cabin (starboard)
31. Band instruments room.
32. Lower conning tower
33. Fan chamber
34. No. 1 boiler room
35. No. 2 boiler room
36. No. 3 boiler room
37. Admiral's galley
38. Admiral's shelter
39. Chart house
40. Conning tower
41. C.P.O. stoker's washplace
42. Dynamo room
43. Engineers workshop
44. Hydraulic engine room
45. Upper dynamo room
46. Lower dynamo room
47. Switchboard room
48. No. 4 boiler room
49. Stokers room
50. Canteen store
51. Engine hatch
52. Seaman's galley

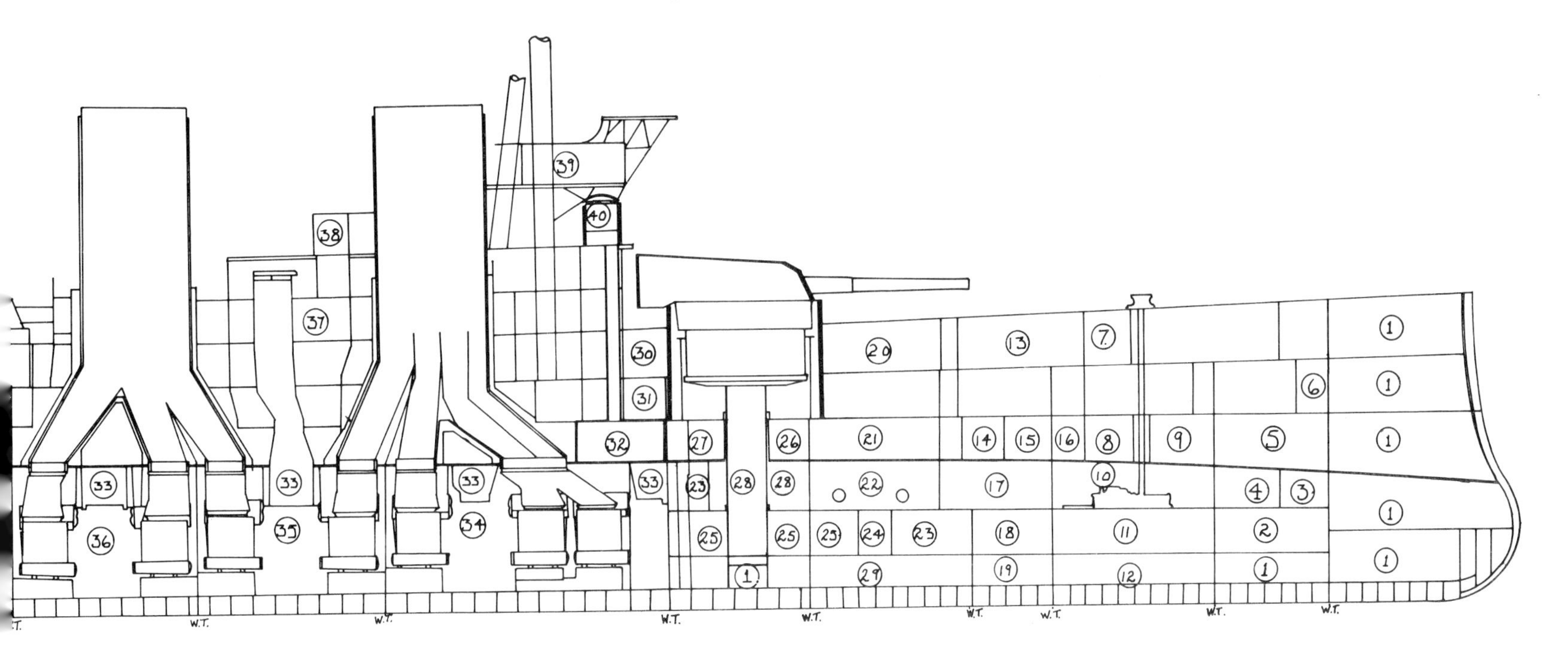

53. Cook's kitchen, officer's galley
54. Bakery
55. Gun room
56. Canteen
57. Issue room
58. Distributing station
59. Fan supply to E.R.
60. Exhaust vents from E.R.
61. Engine room
62. Main condenser
63. L.P. astern turbine
64. L.P. ahead turbine
65. Cruising turbine
66. Handing room
67. Magazine
68. Shell room
69. Shaft
70 Lobby
71. Field gun stowage
72. Fresh water tank
73. Submerged torpedo room
74. Motor generator compartment
75. Submarine mine store
76. Drain tank
77. Prisons
78. Capstan compartment
79. Acid room
80. Hand steering compartment
81. Steering compartment
82. Inflammable store
83. Paint store
84. Paint room
85. Stern torpedo room
86. After conning tower
87. Mess decks

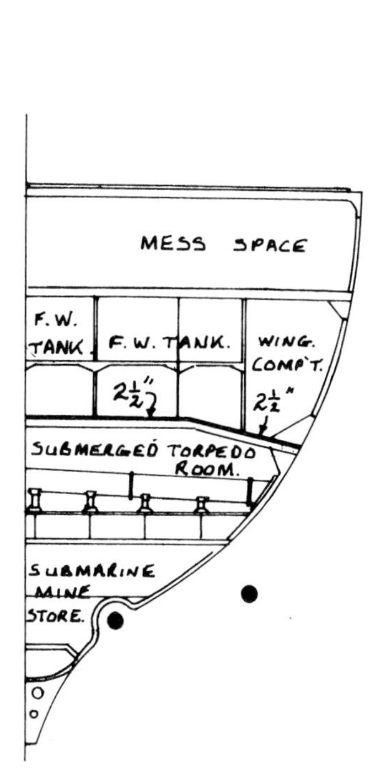

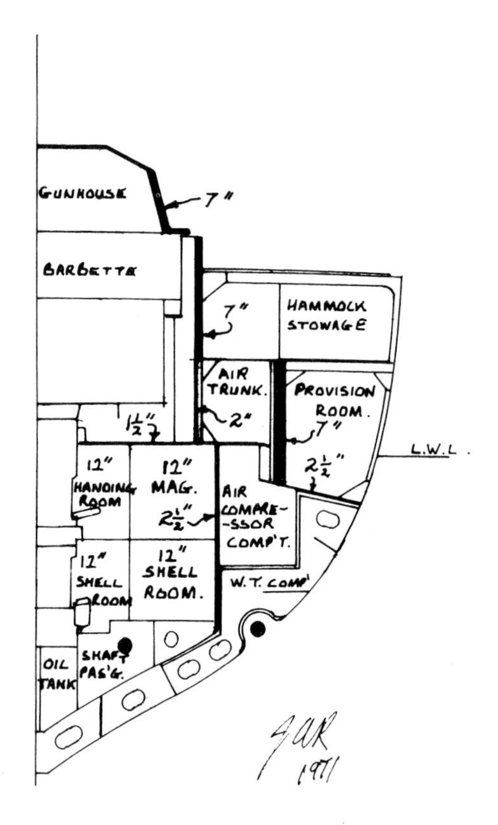

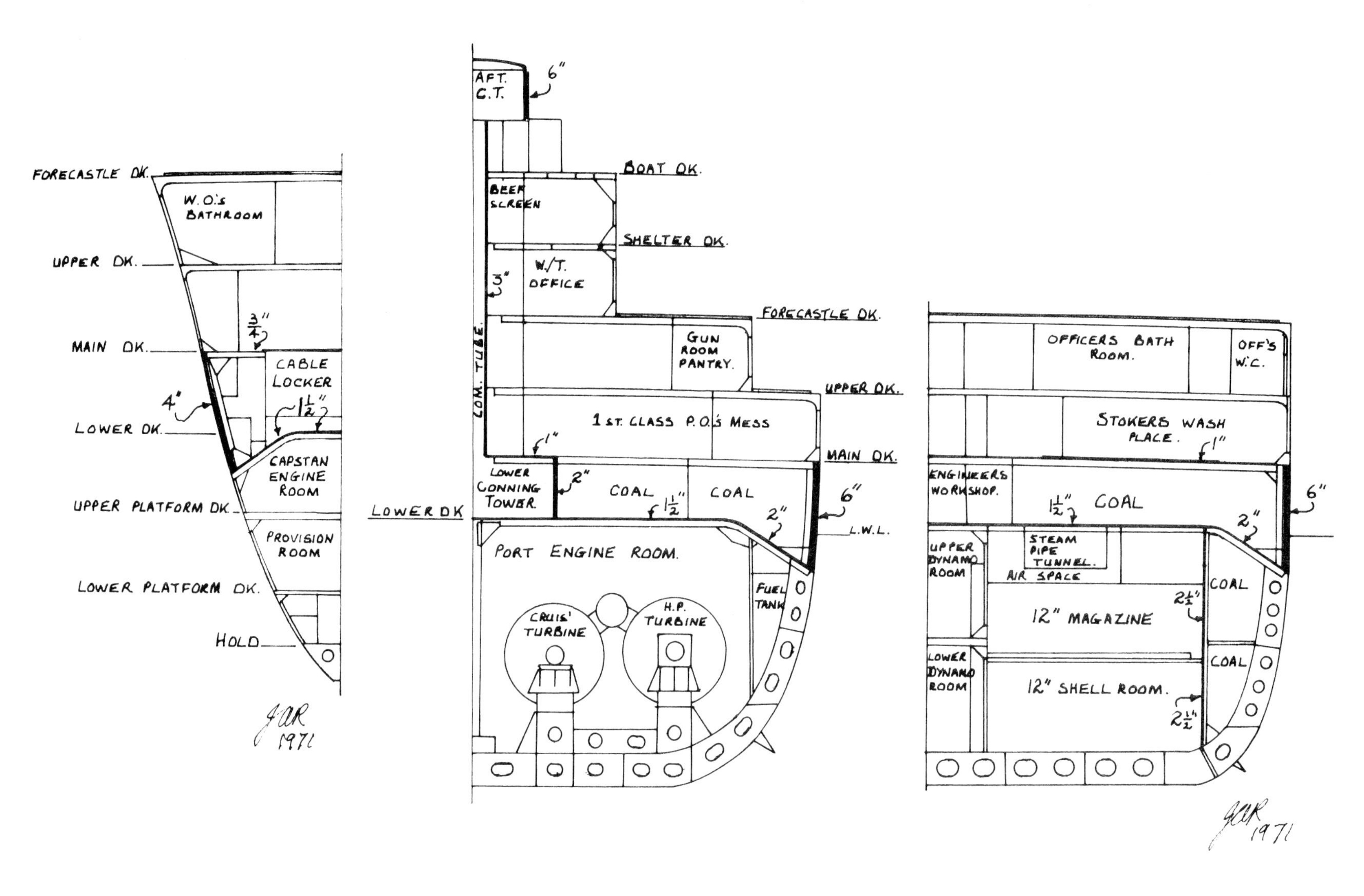

FORECASTLE DK.
W.O.'s BATHROOM
UPPER DK.
MAIN DK.
3/4"
CABLE LOCKER
4"
1 1/2"
LOWER DK.
CAPSTAN ENGINE ROOM
UPPER PLATFORM DK.
PROVISION ROOM
LOWER PLATFORM DK.
HOLD
JAR 1971
AFT. C.T.
6"
BOAT DK.
BEER SCREEN
SHELTER DK.
W/T. OFFICE
3"
COM. TUBE
FORECASTLE DK.
GUN ROOM PANTRY.
UPPER DK.
1st. CLASS P.O.'s MESS
1"
MAIN DK.
LOWER CONNING TOWER
2"
COAL
1 1/2"
COAL
6"
2"
LOWER DK
L.W.L.
PORT ENGINE ROOM.
FUEL TANK
CRUIS' TURBINE
H.P. TURBINE
OFFICERS BATH ROOM.
OFF'S W.C.
STOKERS WASH PLACE.
1"
ENGINEERS WORKSHOP.
1 1/2"
COAL
6"
2"
UPPER DYNAMO ROOM
STEAM PIPE TUNNEL.
AIR SPACE
COAL
2 1/2"
12" MAGAZINE
LOWER DYNAMO ROOM
COAL
12" SHELL ROOM.
2 1/2"
JAR 1971

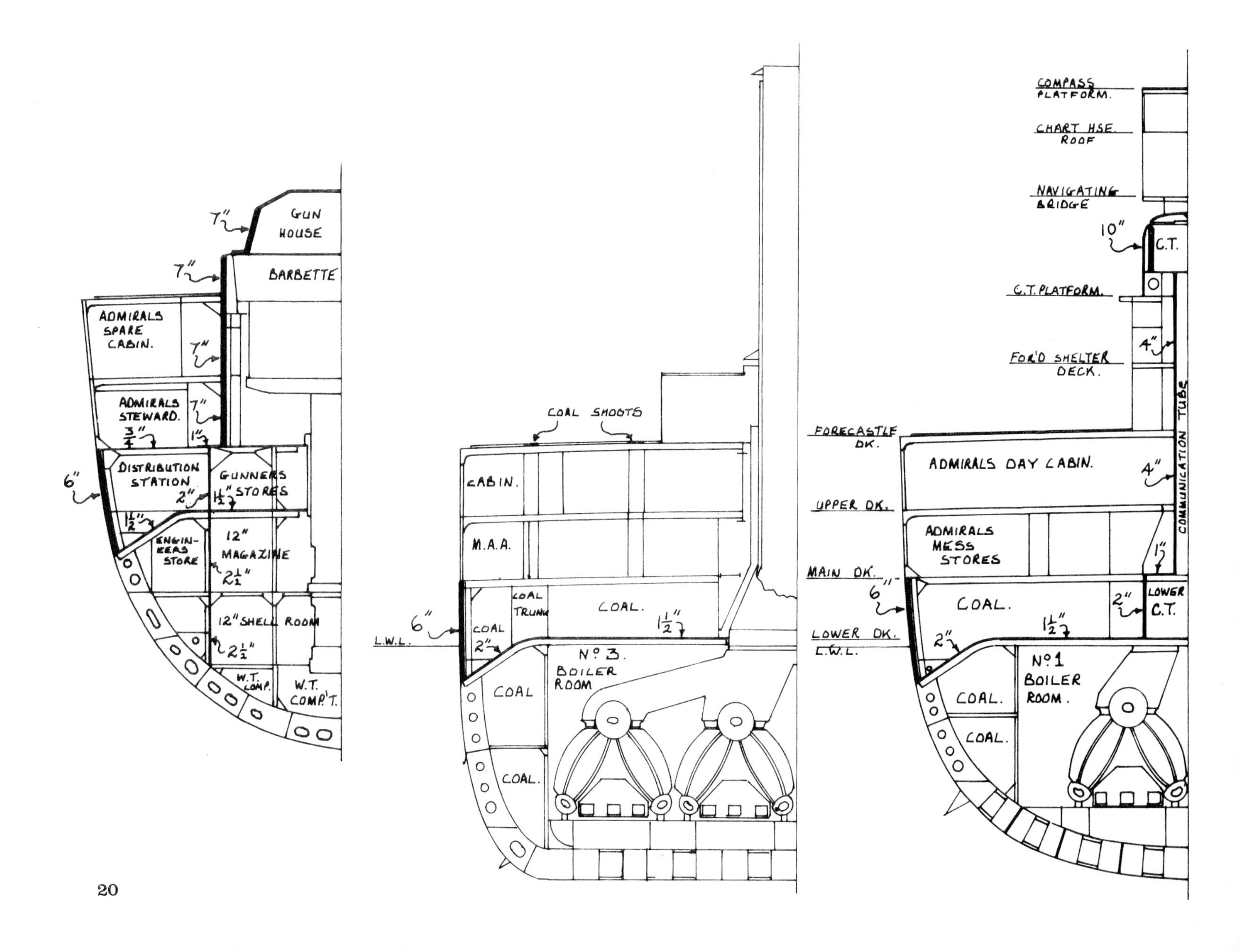

GUN HOUSE
7"
BARBETTE
7"
ADMIRALS SPARE CABIN.
7"
ADMIRALS STEWARD.
7"
3/4"
1"
DISTRIBUTION STATION
GUNNERS STORES
6"
2"
1½"
1½"
ENGINEERS STORE
12" MAGAZINE
2½"
12" SHELL ROOM
2½"
W.T. COMP.
W.T. COMP'T.
COAL SHOOTS
CABIN.
M.A.A.
COAL TRUNK
COAL.
COAL
2"
6"
L.W.L.
1½"
Nº 3. BOILER ROOM
COAL
COAL.
COMPASS PLATFORM.
CHART HSE. ROOF
NAVIGATING BRIDGE
10"
C.T.
C.T. PLATFORM.
4"
FOR'D SHELTER DECK.
COMMUNICATION TUBE
FORECASTLE DK.
ADMIRALS DAY CABIN.
4"
UPPER DK.
ADMIRALS MESS STORES
1"
MAIN DK.
6"
COAL.
2"
LOWER C.T.
LOWER DK.
L.W.L.
2"
1½"
Nº 1 BOILER ROOM.
COAL.
COAL.

INVINCIBLE

Trial	(30 hour (1/5 power	MM 1/5 power	7/10 power	MM Full power	High power cruising	Low power cruising	Intermediate power cruising
Date	22/10/08	/10/08	3/11/08	7/11/08	9/11/08	9/11/08	9/11/08
Place		Chesil Beach	Polperro	Polperro	Polperro	Polperro	
No. of runs		6	6	6	6		
Speed	15.9	16.24	24.26	26.64	20.812	11.55	18.2
SHP	9,301	9,695	34,124	46,500	21,266	3,854	13,291
RPM	170.1	174.3	269.5	295.2	225.62	122.45	196.25

INFLEXIBLE

Trial	(1/5 power (MM	30 hour 1/5 power	Full power	High power cruising
Date	12/6/08	12/6/08	12/6/08	12/6/08
Place			Skelmorlie	Skelmorlie
Speed	16.616	16.53	26.48	20.67
SHP	9,128	9,139	46,947	19,703
RPM	169.6	169	291.3	215

Steering trial – rudders hard over to hard over at 275 revs.

Starboard engine	–	Midships to 35° starboard	–	15 sec
Starboard engine	–	35° starboard to 35° port	–	20 sec
Starboard engine	–	35° port to 35° midships	–	15 sec
Port engine	–	Midships to 35° port	–	13 sec
Port engine	–	35° port to 35° starboard	–	21 sec
Port engine	–	35° starboard to 35° port	–	13½ sec

MACHINERY

Average cost £472,000.
Four sets Parsons direct flow steam turbines.
Thirty one Yarrow large tube boilers (*Indomitable*, Babcock & Wilcox).
S.H.P. – 41,000
Speed – 25.5 knots at load draught, 24.6 knots at deep load.

Radius of Action, at 23 knots

Invincible – 2,270 miles (3,050 using oil fuel)
Inflexible – 2,340 miles (3,110 using oil fuel)
Indomitable – 2,340 miles (3,070 using oil fuel)

Coal Consumption

790 tons per day at full power (*Indomitable* 750 tons per day)
130 tons per day at 10 knots (*Indomitable* 124 tons per day)
Coal at load draught 1000 tons.
Coal (max) 3,000 tons (*Invincible*) 3.084 (*Inflexible*) 3,083 (*Indomitable*)
Fuel oil – 738 tons (*Invincible*) 725 tons (*Inflexible*) 710 tons (*Indomitable*)
Fresh water – 350 tons.

ARMAMENT

Eight – 12 in. Mark X B.L.
Sixteen – 4 in. Mark III Q.F.
Five – .303 in. Maxims .5000 r.p.g. (2 field mountings).
One – field carriage for 4 in. (200 shrapnel shells and 200 full charges.)

	Rudder	Length	Tactical diameter
Powerful	1 — balanced	500′	1,100 yards
Duke of Edinburgh	1 — balanced	480′	740 yards
Dreadnought	2 — balanced	490′	463 yards
Invincible	2 — balanced	530′	

Four — Broadside submerged 18 in. torpedo tubes.
One — stern submerged 18 in torpedo tube.
Twenty three - 18 in. torpedoes.
Six — 14 in. torpedoes for 50′ steam boats.

ARMOUR

Belt — 6 in. (K.C.) amidships, 4 in. (K.C.) forward, none aft.
Bulkheads 7 in. and 6 in. (K.C.).
Barbettes 7 in. (K.C.) 2 in. below level of belt.
Turrets 7 in. (K.C.(sides and faces. 2½ in. (approx) roofs.
C.T. 10 in. (forward 6 in. (aft).
Com. Tube 4 in. (forward) 3 in. (aft).
Lower C.T's 2 in. sides, 1 in. crowns.
Magazine Screens 2½ in.
Decks.
Main deck, ¾ in. forward, 1 in. under forward and midships barbettes.
Lower deck, (forward) 1½ kn. on flats and slopes.
Lower deck, (amidships) 1½ in. on flat, 2 in. on slopes.
Lower deck, (aft) 2½ in. on flats and slopes.
Level of belt above and below water line:—

SEARCH LIGHTS

Eight 36 in. — two on platform abreast fore funnel, two on platform on main mast, two abreast forward C.T., one on port side of amidships funnel, one on starboard side after funnel.
One 24 in. on platform under fore top. The *Invincibles* were originally designed to carry eight 24 in. search lights.

ANCHORS

Bowers. — three 125 cwt Wasteney Smiths stockless.
Stream — one 42 cwt Martins, close stowing.
Kedge. — one 42 cwt Martins, close stowing
Two 5 cwt Admiralty Pattern.

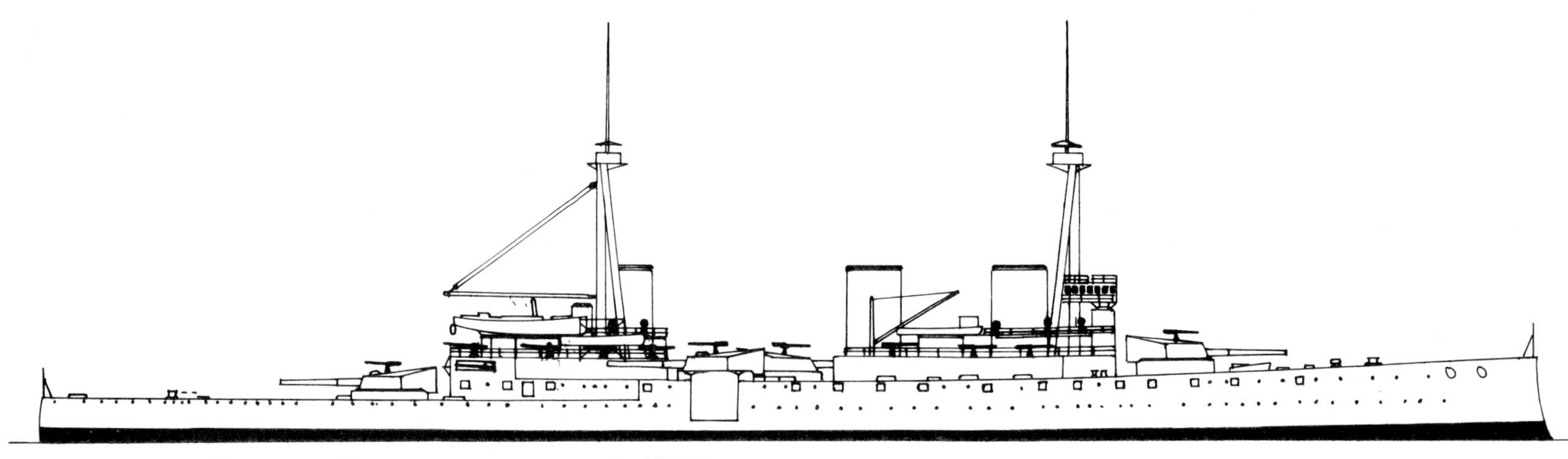

INVINCIBLE CLASS. AS DESIGNED 1905.

Details of the Invincible class as completed

Dimensions	INVINCIBLE	INFLEXIBLE	INDOMITABLE
Displacement at load draught	17,330 tons	17,290 tons	17,410 tons
Displacement at deep load with bunkers & tanks full (excluding oil fuel)	(19,940 tons	19,975 tons	20,125 tons
Weight of hull (as launched)	6,022 tons		5,802.3 tons
Length (pp) 530′ (des)	530′ ¾″	530′ 1″	530′ 1¾″
Length (w.1.) 560′ (des)			
Length (oa) 567′ (des)			
Beam (max) excluding barbette armour	78′8½″	78′10⅛″	78′7¾″
Beam (moulded) 78′6″ (des)	78′5″	78′6⅝″	78′4¼″
Depth 47′8 13/16″ (des)	47′11⅞″		
Draught forward (at load draught)	24′7″	25′1″	25′6″
Draught aft (at load draught)	27′	26′8″	26′7″
Draught at deep load (designed) 29′7″ (aft)			
Tons per inch immersion 69.8			

BOATS

Two 50 ft. steam pinnace (equipped to carry 14 in. torpedoes)
One 40 ft. steam barge (Admirals barge)
One 42 ft. launch.
One 36 ft. sailing pinnace
Three 32 ft. cutters
One 32 ft. galley
One 30 ft. gig
Three 27 ft. whalers
Two 16 ft. dinghy's
One 13½ ft. balsa raft.

The three steam boats, 42ft. launch, 36 ft. sailing pinnace and one whaler were stowed on skid beams over the after shelter deck. The rest were stowed between the forward funnels on skid beams over the forward shelter deck with the exception of two of the 32 ft. cutters which were carried on davits either side of the mainmast and served as sea boats. Davits were also fitted

Aerial view of Inflexible 1917.

	Coal Consumption tons per day	S.H.P.	Speed (knots) Deep Load	Speed (knots) Load Draught	Radius (miles) Normal	Radius (miles) Using Oil Fuel
4/5 power	660	32,800	23.2	24.1		
3/5 power	504	24,600	21.3	22.2	2,650	3,520
2/5 power	370	16,400	18.7	19.3	3,180	4,230
1/5 power	202	8,200	14.8	15.2	4,600	6,020

	Invincible	Inflexible	Indomitable
Above L.W.L.	7′6″	7′5″	7′3″
Below L.W.L.	3′9″	3′10″	4′

to the ships side abreast the bridge on which the 32 ft. galley and 30 ft. gig (starboard side) and a 16 ft. dinghy and 27 ft. whaler (port side) could be stowed when in harbour. (The boats are shown in this position in the main drawing of *Invincible*, in broken outline).

The heavier boats aft were served by the main derrick on the main mast and those forward by two derricks positioned abreast the midships funnel.

H.M.S. Invincible 1907

WIRELESS

Mark 11 W.T. set fitted in all ships.

COMPLEMENT

The numbers in the crew varied and, of course greatly increased during the war, the following figures show the complement at various periods

As designed	722	
Invincible 1908	730	
Indomitable May 1910	795	(as flagship)
Inflexible Oct. 1912	808	(as flagship)
Invincible Aug. 1914	799	(as flagship)
Invincible May 1916	1,032	(as flagship)

ALTERATIONS AND ADDITIONS

Where the exact date is not known the period during which the modification(s) must have taken place are given.

INVINCIBLE

1910–1913 Range drums added to fore and main tops.
1911 Additional yard on fore topmast.
1911–1913 Canvas blast screens fitted to rear of 4 in. guns on roofs of A & Y turrets.
1912–1913 24 in. S.L. on platform under fore top repositioned on roof of Admirals shelter, abaft fore funnel. Two 36 in. search lights added abreast fore funnel at level of boat deck.
1913–1914 Gaff added on main top roof.
March–Aug. 1914 Refit. 23 in. turrets converted to hydraulic power. 4 in. guns on roofs of A & Y turrets removed and re-positioned in forward superstructure. Two 4 in. guns fitted on shelter deck between fore funnels. Two 4 in. guns fitted on C.T. platform abreast forward CT. All 4 in. in forward superstructure enclosed in un-armoured casemates and fitted with shields. Range finder hood fitted on roof of A turret. Gun director fitted on new platform under fore top. Searchlight platform in this position being removed. New fore top, with 9 ft. Argo range finder fitted. Range drums removed. Boat derricks abreast midships funnel moved up to clear 4 in. casemates. Search light platforms at level of navigating bridge extended aft and two more 36 in. search lights fitted. (These were originally fitted abreast fore C.T. and had to be removed to make way for the additional 4 in. guns.) Torpedo nets and booms removed. Bridge remodelled.
Aug–Nov. 1914 Topmasts shortened and spiral range finder baffle fitted to fore topmast.
Jan.–Feb. 1915 Fore funnel raised.
1915 4 in. guns removed from roofs of P & Q turret.
1915–1916 Other modifications not known but it is reasonable to assume that she received alterations similar to those of her sisters including the fitting of 3 in. AA gun(s).

INFLEXIBLE

1910 Range drums fitted on fore and main tops. Temporary flagstaffs added to tops of topgallant masts.
1911 Fore funnel raised.
1912–1913 Canvas blast screens fitted in rear of 4 in. guns on A and Y turrets. Additional yard fitted to fore top mast.
1913–1914 Torpedo nets and booms removed. Flagstaffs fitted to topgallant masts. Additional yard fitted to main top-mast. Gaff fitted to roof of main top. New fore top fitted.
1914 Flagstaffs removed. Four 4 in. on forward shelter deck plated in, in unarmoured casemates.

1915 Gun director fitted on new platform under fore top. 3 in. guns removed from turret roofs. Four 4 in. added in forward superstructure (as *Invincible*) fitted with shields and enclosed in unarmoured case-mates. Searchlight platform at level of navigating bridge extended aft round fore funnel and two 36 in. search lights added. Torpedo net booms replaced but removed 1916. Carley rafts fitted.
Winter 1915–1916 3 in. AA gun fitted on platform at after end of after shelter deck. Range finder fitted on platform abaft after CT. 36 in. search lights by midships and aft funnels removed.
1916 Stern torpedo tube removed.
1916 (After Jutland) Additional armour added to turret roofs, magazine crowns, ammunition hoists and decks around bar-bettes. Magazine flooding arrangements improved and automatic magazine isolation

fitted. 4 in. guns in after superstructure fitted with shields.
1916–1917 Two 3 in. AA fitted, one on port side midships funnel and one on starboard side after funnel.
1917 Gaff repositioned on starfish* 36 in. searchlight platform on mainmast removed and 36 in. searchlights removed from platform around fore funnel. Search lights rearranged as follows:–
Two 36 in. fitted on navigating bridge. One 36 in. fitted on platform at rear end of after shelter deck replacing 3 in. AA gun in that position. Four 36 in. search lights in towers fitted abreast after funnel at base of tripod. 3 in. AA gun beside aft funnel removed. Two small searchlights fitted on raised platform on ex-searchlight platform around fore funnel. Searchlight control positions fitted abreast aft C.T. and fore funnel.
32 ft. cutters and davits on aft' superstructure removed. New bridge platform fitted round fore tripod legs over chart house*. Range finder fitted on platform over chart house. Fore topmast removed and director fitted on fore top roof paravanes fitted. 4 in. AA guns fitted on platform over Admirals shelter between fore funnels.
1917–1918 Aircraft platforms fitted on P & Q turrets. Training scale painted on A & Y turrets. Range clocks fitted on front of fore top and on rear of after shelter deck.
1919–1920 Main topmast shortened. Short fore topmast fitted.

INDOMITABLE

1909 Fitted with submarine sound signalling apparatus.
1910 Fore funnel raised.
1910–1911 Range drums fitted on fore and main tops.
1912–1913 Canvas blast screens fitted in rear of 4 in. guns on A and Y turrets. Two search lights fitted on navigating bridge.
1913 Range drums removed.
1914 Gaff fitted on main top roof. 4 in. guns on roofs of A & Y turrets removed and fitted in forward superstructure, as in *Invincible,* except only the two 4 in. abreast the forward CT were enclosed in unarmoured casemates, rest of battery remained open. All guns in forward superstructure fitted with shields. Torpedo nets and booms removed. Topmasts shortened. New fore top fitted.
1915 Gun director fitted on new platform under fore top. Platform over charthouse enlarged. Searchlight platform at level of navigating bridge extended aft and two 36 in. searchlights added. 4 in. guns removed from roofs of P & Q turrets. Carley rafts fitted.
1915–1916 Two 3 in. AA guns fitted on platforms on port side midships funnel and starboard side after funnel. Searchlights in these positions removed.
1916–1918 As *Inflexible* except for items marked thus*, which were not fitted in *Indomitable.*
1919 Main topgallant and fore topmast added.

COLOUR SCHEMES

Early in the war the Admiralty decided to test a suggestion that warships should be painted with contrasting colours to make range finding difficult. It was not considered possible to carry out this test on a ship of the Grand Fleet and the only large ship then available on a foreign station was the *Indomitable*, under refit at Malta.

In December 1914 she was painted light grey overall with dark grey patches on the hull and superstructure. The scheme was tested off the Malta coast in mid December and reported as unsuccessful. She retained this paint scheme on her return to the Grand Fleet and still carried it at the time of the Battle of Dogger Bank. Shortly after this action the pattern was painted out and she reverted to regulation light grey.

The *Inflexible* while in the Mediterranean in 1915 was also camouflaged, but only partially. White patches were painted on the bow and superstructure, the midships funnel was painted completely white and the other two funnels had dark grey patches. These were painted out when she returned to the Grand Fleet.

In 1915 the *Indomitable* was painted with a large rectangular panel of dark grey along each side to give the impression that another vessel was alongside and thus give a false idea of the ship's speed.

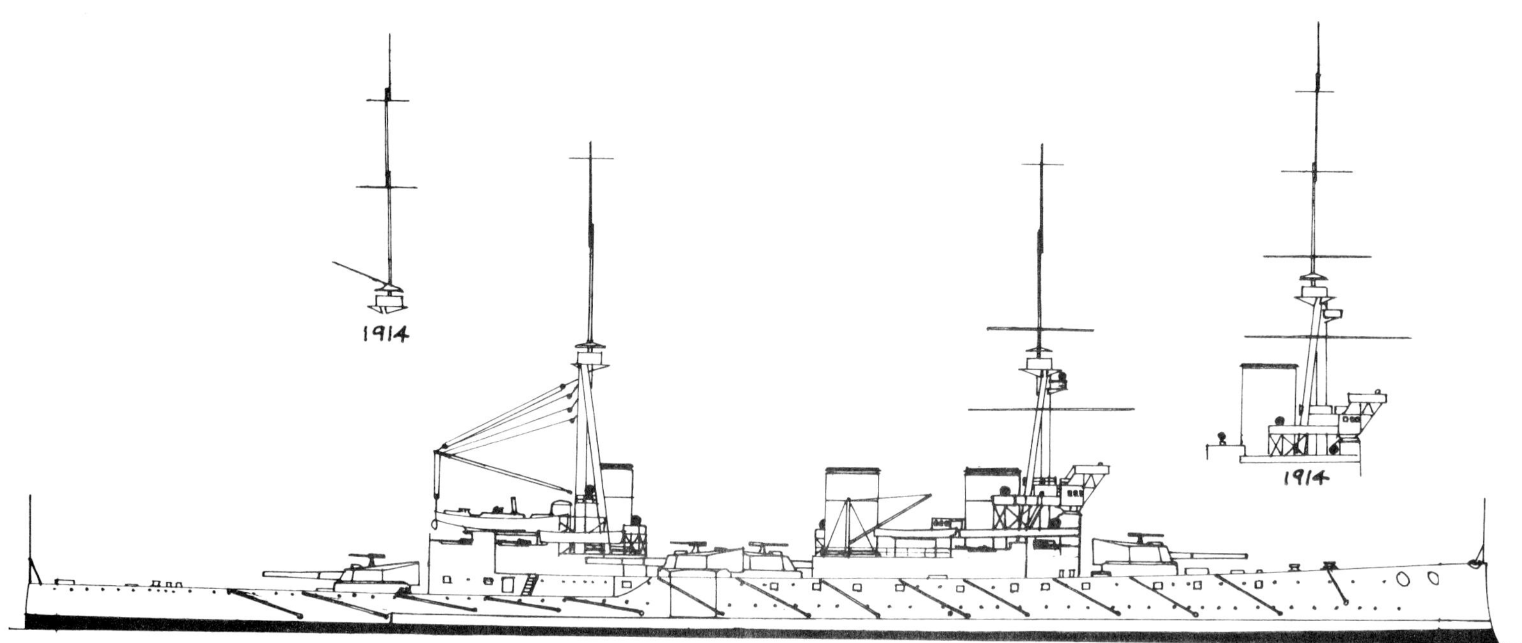

INFLEXIBLE. AS COMPLETED. 1909.

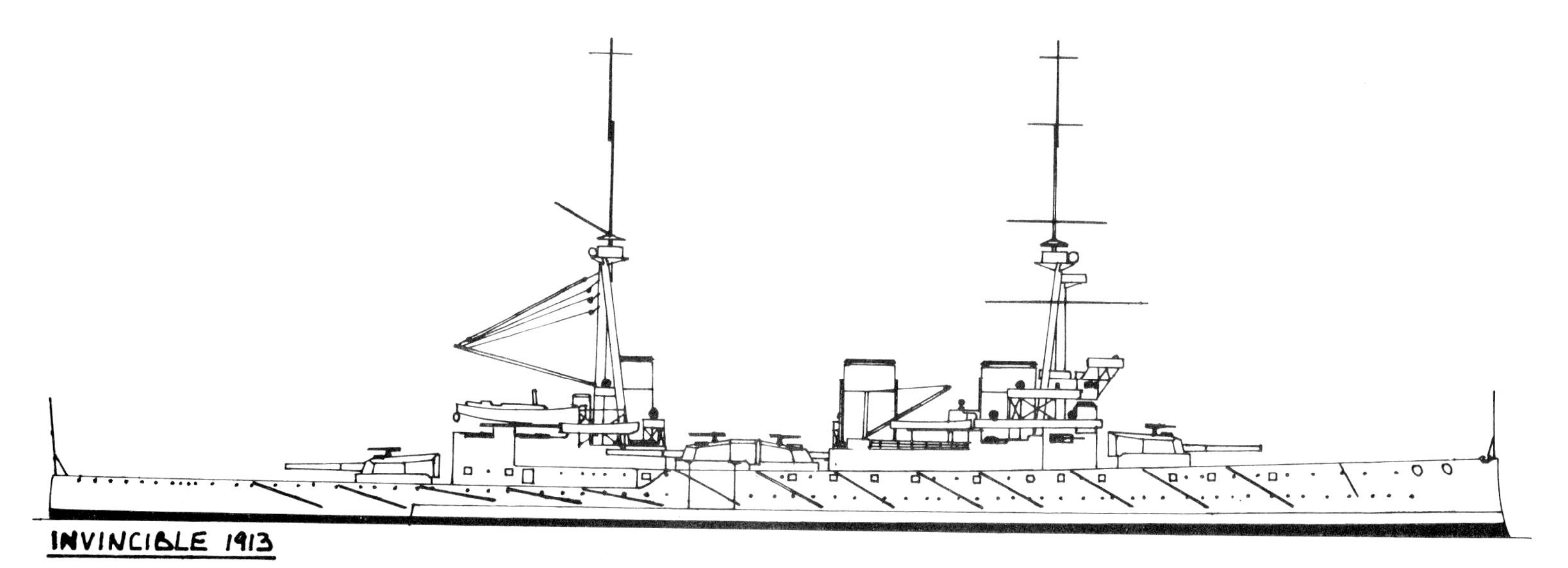

INVINCIBLE 1913

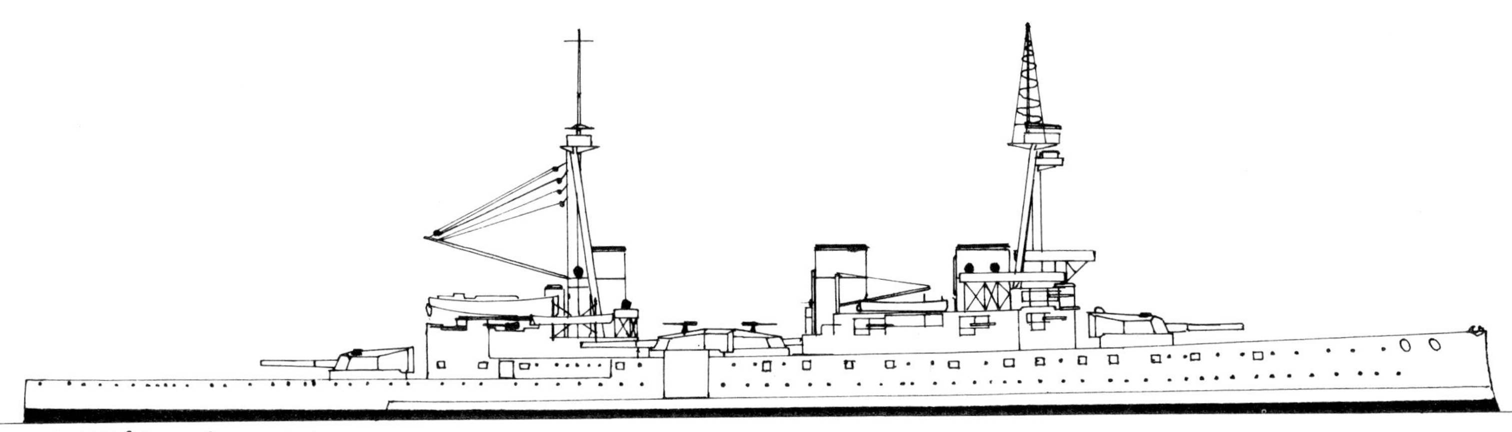

INVINCIBLE Dec. 1914

INDOMITABLE 1914/15

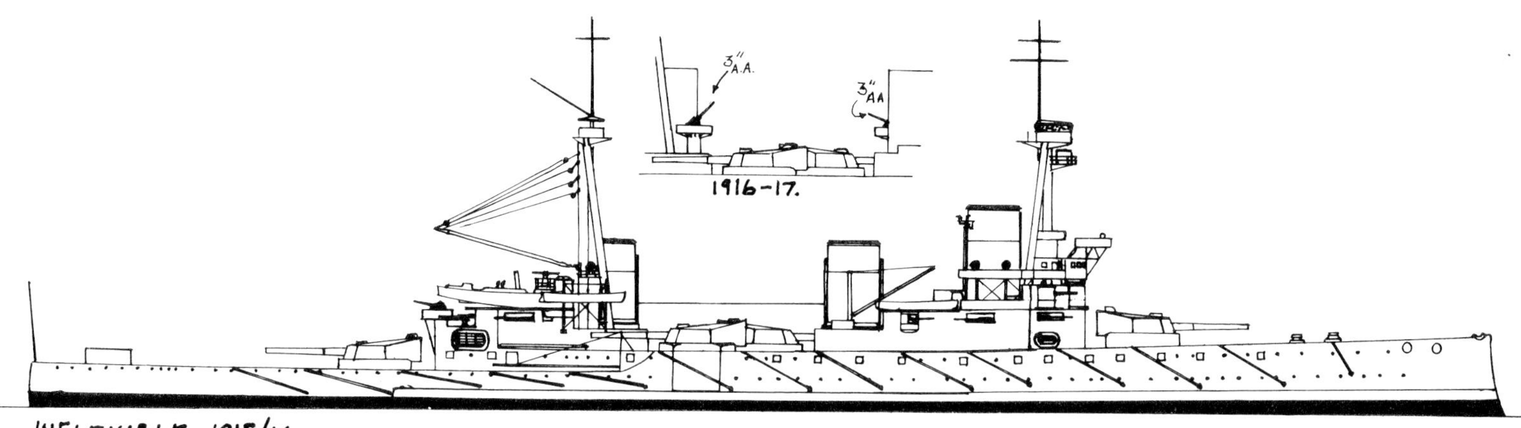

INFLEXIBLE 1915/16

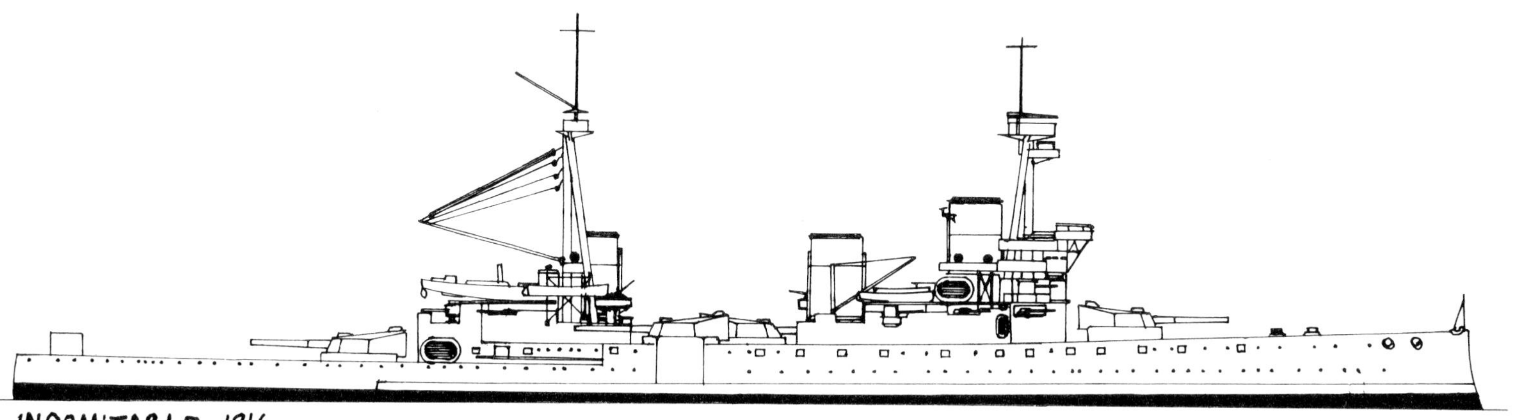

INDOMITABLE 1916

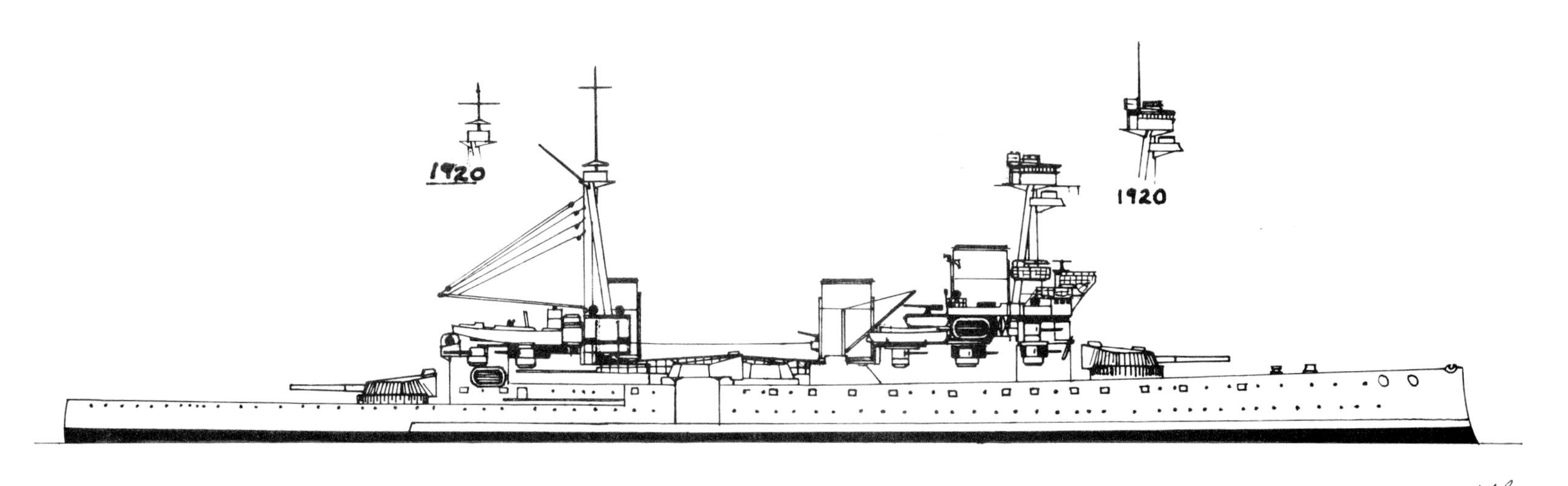

INFLEXIBLE 1918

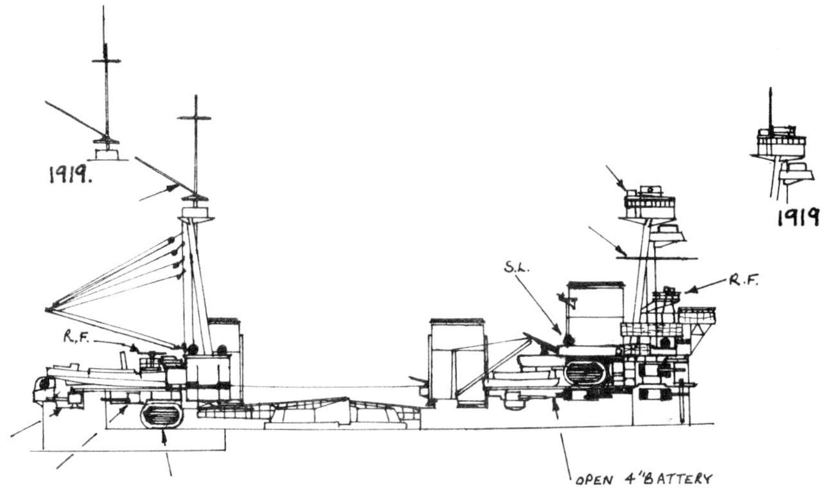

INDOMITABLE 1918

DIFFERANCES ARROWED

Indomitable raising steam shortly after completion in 1908.

Dispositions

INDOMITABLE

1st of name. Battle honours – Dogger Bank 1915, Jutland 1916. Built by Fairfield S.B. Co., Glasgow. Cost – £1,662,337 (excluding guns). Laid down – March 1907. Launched 16 March 1907

Commissioned – 20 Jun. 1908 at Portsmouth by Capt. H.G. King-Hall for detached service to carry the Prince of Wales to Canada for the tercentenary celebrations at Quebec. End of July, sailed for Canada in company with *Minotaur*.

August returned to U.K. and taken in hand by the contractors at Chatham for completion.

28 Oct. 1908 Transferred from contract and joined Nore division, Home Fleet.

April 1909, joined the 1st C.S. *(Drake*, (flag), *Invincible, Indomitable* and *Inflexible)* attached to 1st division, Home fleet.

July *Defence* joined the 1st C.S.

26 July 1909 Flag ship to 1st C.S. (Rear Admiral Sir S.C.J. Colville) transferred from *Drake* to *Indomitable.* Captain C.M. de Bartolome appointed.

1910 Refit at Chatham.

8 Aug. 1910 Paid off at Chatham.

9 Aug. 1910 Recommissioned as flagship 1st C.S.

3 Jan. 1911 Captain A.A.M. Duff appointed flag captain, 1st C.S.

24 Feb. 1911 Rear Admiral Colville relieved by Rear Admiral Lewis Bayly as Commander 1st C.S.

Battlecruiser 1906/1907 Programme. Built by Armstrong at Elswick 1906–1908. General arrangement as in August 1914.

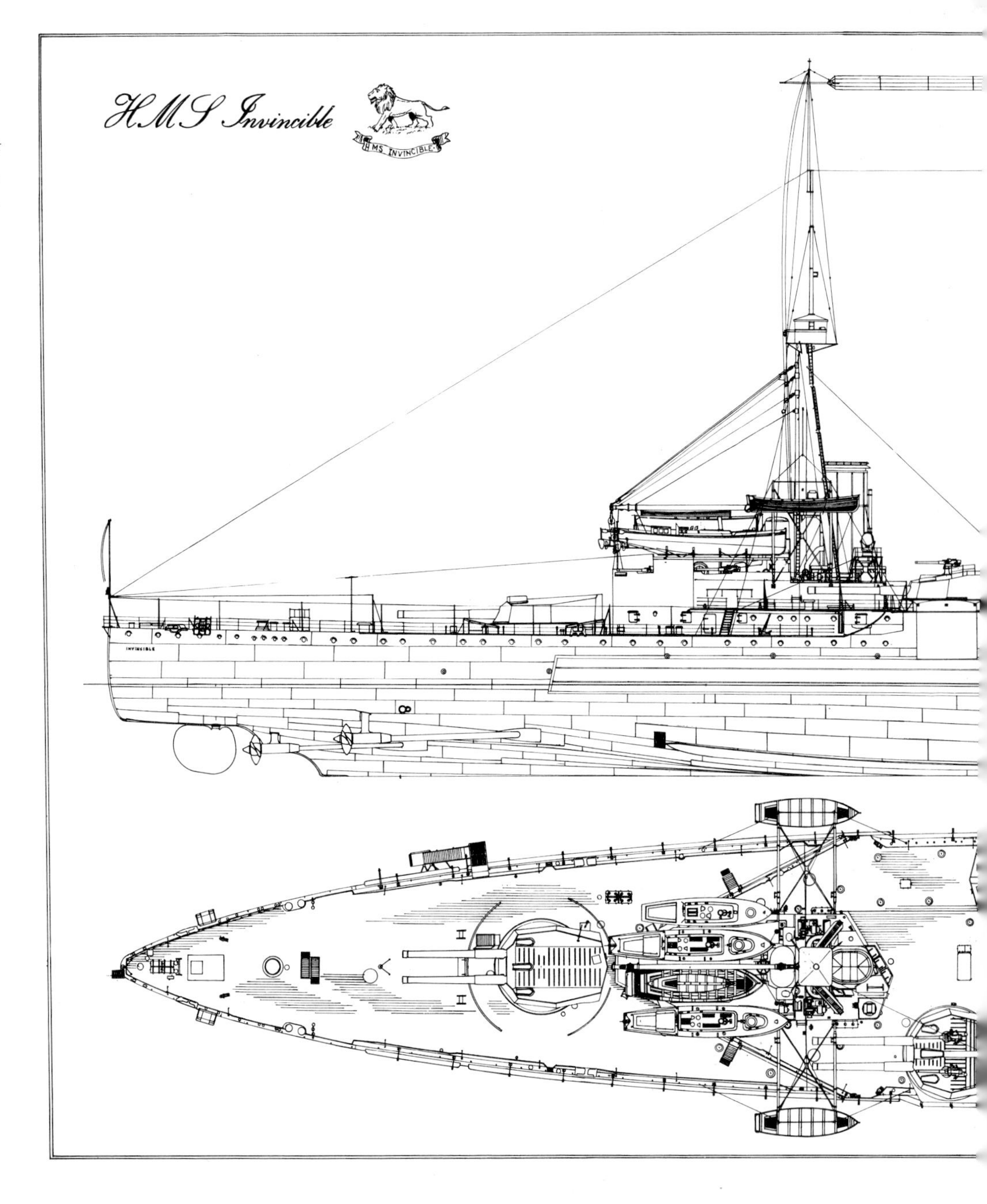

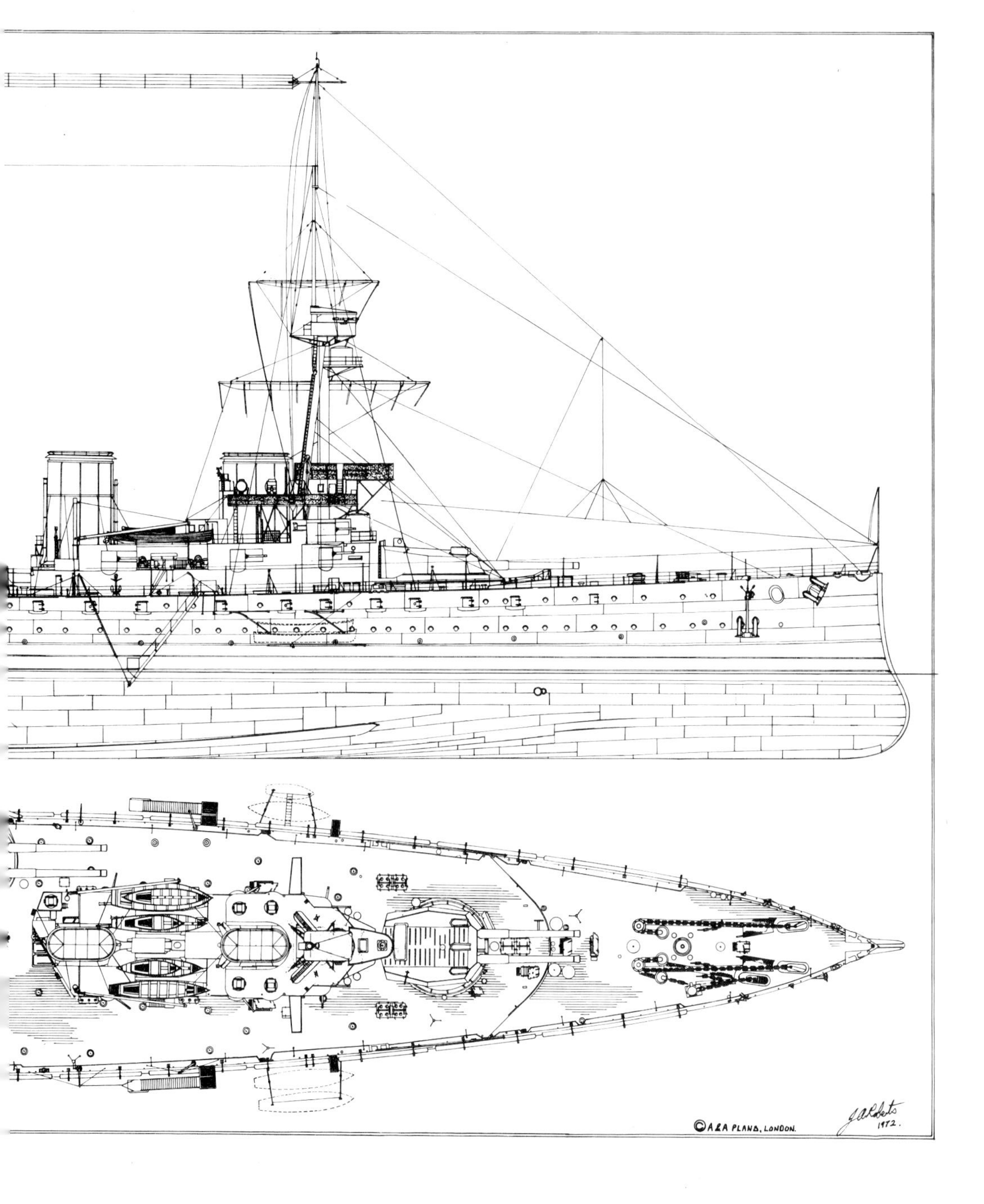
©A&A PLANS, LONDON.
1972.

Nov. 1911 Paid off for refit, reduced to nucleus crew.
21 Feb. 1912 Recommissioned by Captain G.H. Baird for service as flagship 2nd C.S., Home fleet (*Achilles, Cochrane, Natal, Warrior,* and *Shannon).*
5 Mar. 1912 Hoisted flag Rear Admiral Sir George Warrender, commander 2nd C.S., transferred from *Shannon.*
Dec. 1912 Relieved as flagship 2nd C.S. by *Shannon.*
11 Dec 1912 Temporarily attached to 1st C.S. (*Lion*, flag ship Admiral Bayly, *Princess Royal, Indefatigable* and *Invincible)* as a private ship, Captain F.W. Kennedy appointed.
Jan. 1913 1st C.S. became 1st B.C.S.
March 1913 Rear Admiral Beatty appointed Commander 1st B.C.S.
Aug. 1913 With *Invincible* transferred to Mediterranean to form 2nd B.C.S.
Dec. 1913 *Invincible* returned to U.K.,

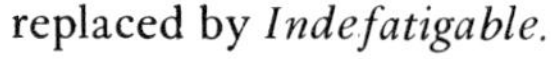

replaced by *Indefatigable.*
10 Feb. 1914 Recommissioned for 2nd B.C.S.
July 1914 Taken in hand for refit at Malta.
27 July 1914 Ordered out of dock before completion of refit due to situation in Europe.
2–4 Aug. 1914 Search for *Goeben* and *Breslau* in company with *Indefatigable.*
4 Aug. 1914 Shadowing *Goeben* and *Breslau.*
5 Aug. 1914 Rendezvous with *Inflexible* off Pantellaria Island, ordered to coal at Bizerta.
6 Aug. 1914 Sailed from Bizerta and joined *Inflexible* and *Indefatigable* at Malta.
8 Aug. 1914 sailed from Malta with *Inflexible, Indefatigable* and *Weymouth.*
10–11 Aug. 1914 Searching for *Goeben* in the Agean sea.
12 Aug. 1914 Blockading the Dardanelles (*Goeben* & *Breslau* having entered there) with *Indefatigable* and *Weymouth).*
19 Aug. 1914 Ordered to leave the Dardenelles blockade.
20 Aug. 1914 Sailed for Gibraltar.
Sept. 1914 Returned to Dardenelles blockade.
3 Nov. 1914 Bombarded outer defences of the Dardenelles. With *Indefatigable* fired on Sedd el Bahr and Cape Helles, the two battle cruisers firing 46 12 in. shells. Magazine at Sedd el Bahr blew up.

Left: Invincible in 1910. Note the range indicator drums on the fore and main tops.

Right: Inflexible 1915. Note the unusual camouflage.

Dec. 1914 Ordered home to join Grand Fleet.
23 Dec. 1914 Received orders to rendezvous with battle cruisers E.N.E. of Firth of Forth.
26 Dec. 1914 Joined battle cruiser squadron.
Dec. 1914–Jan. 1915 Refit.
15 Jan. 1914 Formed 2nd B.C.S. with *New Zealand*, (Flag Vice Admiral Sir G. Moore)
24 Jan. 1915 Battle of Dogger Bank.
Feb.–Mar. 1915 Under refit after a fire caused by an electrical fault.
11 Mar. 1915 On the return journey to Rosyth sighted a U Boat off Montrose preparing to attack. Forced U boat to dive and saw no more of it.
Mar. 1915 Joined B.C.S. *(Invincible)* at Rosyth.
May 1915 Rear Admiral Hood became Commander 3rd B.C.S. with his flag in *Invincible.*
June 1915 *Inflexible* joined 3rd B.C.S.
May 1916 3rd B.C.S. joined Grand Fleet at Scapa Flow for gunnery exercises.

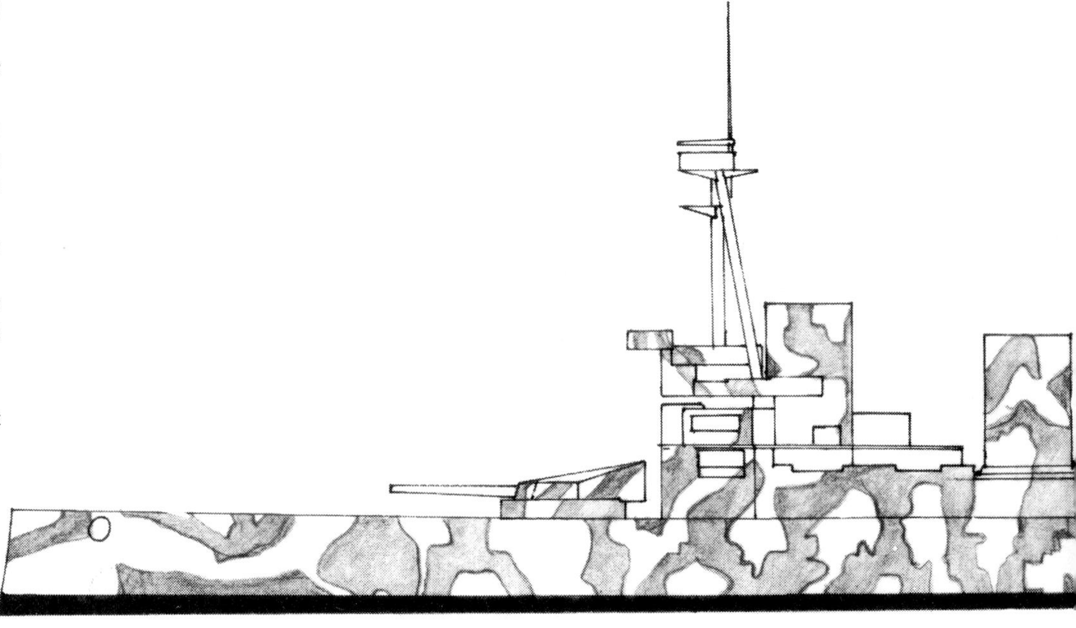

INDOMITABLE. CAMOUFLAGE DEC 1914 – FEB 1915

May 31–June 1 1916 Battle of Jutland.
2 June 1916 Entered Firth of Forth.
5 June 1916 2nd B.C.S. *(Indomitable, Inflexible, Australia)*
End 1916 Captain Kennedy relieved by Captain Hodges.
Nov. 1918 Surrender of German Fleet.
Jan. 1919 Left 2nd B.C.S.
Feb. 1919 Nore Reserve (flag ship until July 1919).
31 Mar. 1920 Paid off.
1 Dec. 1921 Sold to Stanlee, Dover.
30 Aug. 1922 Arrived at Dover for breaking up.

INFLEXIBLE

5th vessel of name. Battle honours – Lake Champlain 1776, Cuddalore 1783, Egypt 1801, Baltic 1807, New Zealand 1845–57, Black Sea 1854–1855, China 1856–60, Fatshan Creek 1857, Alexandria 1882

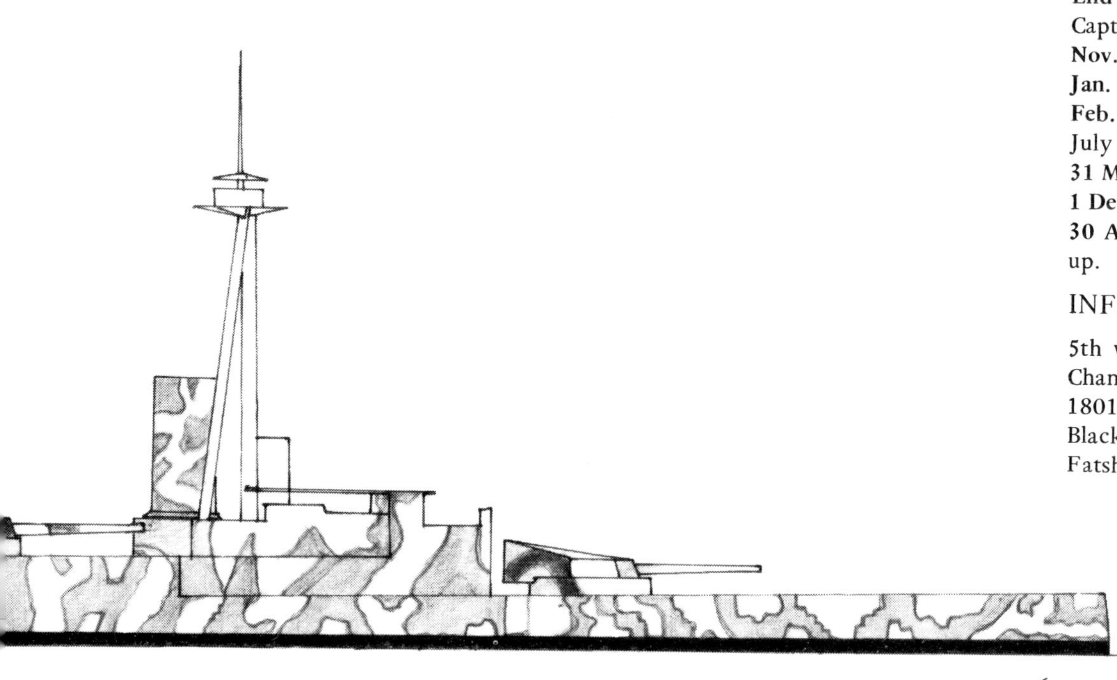

Falklands 1914, Dardenelles 1915, Jutland 1916, Built by John Brown at Clydebank. Cost –£1,630,739 (excluding guns) Laid down 5 Feb. 1906. Launched 26 June 1907. Completed 20 Oct. 1908.

1 June 1908 Captain H.H.T. Torlesse appointed.

20 Oct 1908 Commissioned at Chatham by Captain Torlesse to replace *Jupiter* in Nore Division of Home Fleet.

Oct. 1908–Jan 1909 Refit and repair at Chatham, after damage caused by gun trials.

Jan. 1909 Nore division Home Fleet.

Mar. 1909 Joined 1st C.S. on its formation. 1st C.S. attached to 1st division Home Fleet. Slight bunker explosion – one stoker injured, no structural damage.

13 Sept. 1909 While training P turret, walking pipe and fittings damaged.

16 Sept. 1909 Flagship Admiral of Fleet, Sir E.H. Seymour for visit to New York at time of Hudson–Fulton celebrations, until October.

11 Oct. 1909 paid off for repair and refit until December 1909.

14 Dec. 1909 Capt. C.L. Napier appointed.

11 Oct. 1910 Paid off and recommissioned on 12 Oct. at Chatham.

26 May 1911 In collision with *Bellerophon* off Portland. Bows damaged. Blame attributed to *Bellerophon.*

1911 Refit.

18 Nov. 1911 Became flag Rear Admiral Bayly, commander 1st C.S. during refit of *Indomitable.*

8 May 1912 Relieved as flagship 1st C.S by *Lion* and Capt. R.S. Phipps Hornby appointed.

4 Nov. 1912 Paid off at Chatham.

5 Nov. 1912 Recommissioned at Chatham by Capt. A.N. Loxley as flagship Admiral A. Berkley Milne, C. in C. Mediterranean Fleet, in place of the *Good Hope.*

July 1914 Sailed with Med. fleet to Alexandria.

28 Jul. 1914 Left Alexandria for Malta.

30 July 1914 Arrived Malta.

4–5 Aug. 1914 On patrol in Malta channel.

5 Aug. 1914 Rendezvous with *Indomitable* and *Indefatigable* off Pantellaria Island.

5–6 Aug. 1914 On patrol with *Indefatigable* between N. Africa and Sardinia in hope of intercepting *Goeben.*

6 Aug. 1914 Arrived Malta to coal, joined by *Indomitable.*

8 Aug. Sailed from Malta.

10–11 Aug. 1914 Searching for *Goeben* in Aegean Sea.

12 Aug. 1914 Blockading Dardenelles. Milne ordered home.

13 Aug. 1914 Sailed for Malta.

18 Aug. 1914 Left Malta for home.

19 Aug. 1914 Ordered to Humber.

28 Aug. 1914 Capt. F. Philimore appointed.

Sept. 1914 Joined *Invincible* at Rosyth in 2nd B.C.S. replacing *New Zealand.*

1–10 Oct. 1914 On patrol in Shetland Faeroes Passage during passage of 1st Canadian Troop convoy.

18 Oct. 1914 2nd B.C.S. and division of destroyers ordered to Heligoland Bight to support air raid on Cuxhaven Zeppelin sheds.

25 Oct. 1914 Raid abandoned due to bad weather.

4 Nov. 1914 Ordered to South America.

5 Nov. 1914 Sailed with *Invincible* from Cromarty for Berehaven to coal but diverted to Devonport.

8 Nov. 1914 Arrived Devonport.

8–11 Nov 1914 Repairs at Devonport.

7 Dec. 1914 Arrived Port William, Falkland Islands.

8 Dec. 1914 Battle of Falkland Islands, search for *Dresden.*

19 Dec. Ordered home.

24 Jan. 1915 Relieved *Indefatigable* as flagship Admiral Carden C. in C. Med. off Dardenelles.

Jan–Mar. 1915 Dardanelles blockade and bombardment of coastal forts.

Feb. 1915 Admiral Carden relieved by Admiral de Robeck.

19 Mar. 1915 Attack on the narrows. Struck mine and retired badly damaged.

Mar.–May 1915 Repairs carried out at Gibraltar.

19 June 1915 Joined 3rd B.C.S. (*Indomitable* & *Invincible*) at Rosyth.

1916 Capt. Heaton-Ellis appointed (May or before)

31 May–Jun 1 1916 Battle of Jutland.

19 Aug. 1916 Attacked by U 65 but not hit.

1 Feb. 1918 Collided with K22 off May Island. No damage to *Inflexible.*

Nov. 1918 Surrender of German fleet.

Jan. 1919 Nore reserve.
31 Mar. 1920 Paid off.
1 Dec. 1921 Sold to Stanlee, Dover for scrapping.

INVINCIBLE

6th vessel of name. Battle honours – St. Vincent 1780, Chesapeake 1781, St. Kitts 1782, 1st of June 1794, Trinidad 1797, Alexandria 1882, Heligoland 1914. Falklands 1914, Jutland 1916.
Built by Messrs Armstrong, Whitworth & Co. at Newcastle. Cost £1,677,415 (excluding guns). Laid down 2nd April 1906. Launched 13 Apr. 1907, Completed Mar. 1909.
8 Sept. 1908 Capt. M.E.F. Kerr appointed. Completion delayed by installation of electric turrets.
20 Mar. 1909 Commissioned at Portsmouth for 1st C.S. attached to 1st Division Home Fleet.
1909–1910 Repairs, alterations and additions at Portsmouth.
27 Mar. 1911 Reduced to nucleus crew prior to being taken in hand at Portsmouth for refit and alterations.
28 Mar. 1911 Capt. R.P.F. Purefoy appointed.
Mar.–May 1911 Refit.
16 Mar 1911 Recommissioned at Portsmouth for further service in 1st C.S.
1 May 1912 Capt. M. Culme-Seymour appointed.
1 Jan. 1913 1st B.C.S.
17 Mar. 1913 Collided with submarine C.34 in Stokes Bay, no damage.
Aug. 1913 Transferred to Mediterranean after manoeuvres, Capt. H.B. Pelly appointed.
Oct. 1913 At Cartagena during visit of the President of the French Republic to the King of Spain.
Dec. 1913 Left Med. for home.
Mar. 1914 Paid off for refit until Aug. 1914.
1 Aug. 1914 Capt. C.M. de Bartolme appointed.
3 Aug. 1914 Commissioned at Portsmouth and ordered to Queenstown in case of break out by enemy battlecruisers.
12 Aug. 1914 Hoisted flag of Rear Admiral Sir Archibald Moore.
19 Aug. 1914 Ordered to Humber, joined *New Zealand* forming 2nd B.C.S.
28 Aug. 1914 With *New Zealand* acted as supports for raid on Heligoland Bight.
Sept. 1914 Moved to Rosyth, *New Zealand* replaced by *Inflexible* on her return from Med.
1 Oct. 1914 2nd B.C.S. reconstituted (*Invincible* and *Inflexible*)
2–10 Oct. 1914 On patrol between Shetlands and Faeroes during passage of 1st Canadian troop convoy.
18 Oct 1914 2nd B.C.S. and division of destroyers ordered to Heligoland Bight to support air raid on Cuxhaven Zeppelin sheds.
25 Oct. 1914 Raid cancelled due to bad weather.
4 Nov. 1914 Ordered to South America.
5 Nov. 1914 Sailed from Cromarty with *Inflexible* for Berehaven to coal. Diverted to Devonport en route.
8 Nov. 1914 Arrived Devonport.
9 Nov. 1914 Hoisted flag Admiral Sturdee, flag Capt. P.T.H. Beamish.
11 Nov. 1914 Sailed for Falkland Islands.
7 Dec. 1914 Arrived Port William, Falkland Islands.
8 Dec. 1914 Battle of Falkland Islands. Search for *Dresden*.
16 Dec. 1914 Sailed for home, diverted en route to Gibraltar.
11 Jan 1915 Arrived at Gibraltar for docking, alterations and repairs.
End Feb. 1915 Arrived at Scapa for gunnery exercises.
Early Mar. 1915 Joined BCF at Rosyth. Joined by *Indomitable* in Mar. and *Inflexible* in June, forming 3rd B.C.S.
Apr. 1915 Sent to Tyne to change some of her 12 in. guns which had been worn during action off the Falklands.
26 May 1915 Hoisted flag Rear Admiral Hood 3rd B.C.S.
May 1916 Refit.
May 1916 3rd B.C.S. went to Scapa Flow for gunnery exercises.
31 May 1916 Battle of Jutland (Capt. A.L. Cay) 18.32 under heavy fire, from enemy battlecruisers & battle ships, blew up and sank.

Notes on War Service

THE BATTLE OF THE FALKLAND ISLANDS – 8 Dec. 1914

The main part of this action was fought between the *Invincible* (flagship of Admiral

Sturdee) and the *Inflexible* and the German armoured cruisers, *Scharnhorst* (flagship of Admiral Von Spee) and *Gneisnau* in the South Atlantic. The sea was calm, the sky was clear and visibility good. The British ships possessed a broadside of 5,100 lbs, against 1,957 lbs in the German vessels and a superiority in speed of about 4 knots.

The main action commenced at a range of 14,000 yards, the maximum range of the battlecruisers being 16,400 yards and that of the German 8.2 in. guns, 13,500 yards. The enemy attempted to keep the range down to 12,000 yards in order to bring their 5.9 in. weapons into action and at one point succeeded in reducing it to 11,000 yards. The fire of the British ships was seriously hampered by their own funnel smoke which obscured the enemy from the gun layers view, Von Spee having taken up the lee position.

After being in action for about three hours, the *Scharnhorst* listed over to port until she was on her beam ends and then sank, there were no survivors. The *Gneisenau* continued to fight for almost another two hours until her motive power was gone and she had expended all her ammunition. The order was then given for her to be scuttled. She slowly heeled over and rapidly sank. She had been hit by at least fifty 12 in. shells.

The German shells, being fired from extreme range tended to come down on the British ships at a steep angle. The *Inflexible* was hit three times by enemy shells receiving little damage but suffering one seaman killed and two wounded. The *Invincible* was hit by twenty two shells, the majority being 8.2 in. One shell made a large hole in the deck and wrecked the ward room. Another 8.2 in. hit a 4 in. gun, completely destroying it, and then plunged down through three decks before coming to rest in the Admiral's still room, without exploding. The 7 in. front plate of A turret was hit between the two guns but only slightly dented. There was a hole in her side just forward of Q turret, one of the legs of the fore tripod was shot away and a number of ratings messes were wrecked. *Invincible* was hit twice below the water line. One shell went under the belt and exploded in a 100 tons bunker adjacent to the magazine of one of the midships turrets. The magazine screens and the coal absorbed the explosion but the bunker rapidly flooded. The corresponding bunker on the opposite side of the ship was flooded to compensate. The second under water hit was on the stem and flooded the water tight compartment in the bows. Remarkably the *Invincible* suffered no casualties except for Commander Townsend who was slightly wounded by a splinter. Both battlecruisers expended almost 600 12 in. shells each, during this action out of a total shell compliment of 640. The nearest stock from which they could replenish was at Gibraltar. In all other respects at the end of the day the two British ships were still fit for action.

THE BATTLE OF DOGGER BANK—24th JANUARY 1915

The *Indomitable* was the only member of the class involved in this action, which consisted of a long stern chase. Being in the rear of the British line and the slowest member of the force she did not open fire until late in the battle. Having worked up to 26 knots she earned herself a congratulatory signal from Admiral Beatty in the flagship *Lion.*

The *Lion* was put out of action at a crucial point in the battle resulting in the escape of all the German vessels with the exception of the armoured cruiser *Bleucher* which sank after being hit by 70 shells and 7 torpedoes.

The *Lion*, with 3,000 tons of water in her, was down by the bows and listing to port. Her port engine was out of action and the starboard engine was giving trouble. At 03.38 on the morning of the 25th the *Indomitable* was ordered to take the *Lion* in tow. After not inconsiderable difficulties the *Indomitable* towed the *Lion* into the Forth on the 26th. The flagships starboard engine had eventually stopped quite early in the tow and she had been using hand steering, having no steam, she was six feet down by the bows and listing about 15 degrees.

One very important lesson was learnt by the Germans during this action. A British shell had exploded in one of the after barbettes of the German flagship *Seydlitz.*

Inflexible 1918. In her final wartime guise.

The explosion ignited some cordite charges which flashed down the turret trunk and then up into the next turret putting both turrets out of action. Had it not been for the rapid flooding of the magazines these may well have detonated and destroyed the ship. Thus the Germans learn a year before Jutland about the dangers of cordite fires and equipped their ships with automatic magazine isolation.

THE MINING OF INFLEXIBLE — 18th MARCH 1915

On the 18 Mar. the *Inflexible* accompanied an allied naval force attempting to force a passage through the Dardanelles. This involved the engagement of land forts and thus placed the warships at a considerable disadvantage. The *Inflexible* was one of the early casualties.

At 12.20 the foremast was hit by a shell which set the forebridge and the charthouse on fire. She was hit several more times within the next few minutes receiving a hit on one of her turrets. At 12.27 the fore top was reported as out of action. One shell exploded on her fore signal yard and sent splinters down through the roof and side of the fire control position. She retired to put out her fires and returned to the action later in the day:

◁ *Indomitable 1910. A stern view in Chatham Dockyard.*

At 16 00 she struck a mine which exploded against the starboard bow at the level of the fore torpedo flat. The explosion made a hole 30 feet long by 26 feet deep and flooded about twenty compartments including the torpedo flat, the forward magazine and Number 1 boiler room. She immediately took a list to starboard, all her lights went out and the ventilators ceased to operate. Four men, (Lt. Com. Acheson, Sub. Lt. Giles, Chief ERA 2nd class Snowdon and Stoker 1st class Davidson) went down into the forward magazine and shell room after the crews of these compartments had been driven out by fumes. They shut off valves and closed water tight doors with the lights out. The shell room had 2 foot of water in it which was rising rapidly and the magazine was flooding slowly.

The ventilators and the lights in the machinery spaces having gone the engine room staff had to work in semi darkness and in considerable discomfort from the heat. Having withdrawn from the Dardenelles the *Inflexible* made for Tenedos. Fortunately her bulkheads held under the strain and she anchored about 1½ hours later. At the commencement of the action the *Inflexible's* displacement was 21,250 tons, her draught on her return showed that she had shipped 1,600 tons of water through the damaged side.

THE BATTLE OF JUTLAND – 31st MAY TO 1st JUNE 1916

At the end of May the 3rd B.C.S. – *Invincible* (flagship Admiral Hood), *Indomitable* and *Inflexible* were stationed

▽ *Indomitable 1910 in Chatham Dockyard after having the fore funnel raised to keep the funnel gases clear of the bridge. Note the white recognition band on the third funnel. All three carried these from 1910 until 1914.*

with the Grand Fleet at Scapa Flow. When the battle fleet put to sea on 30 May Jellecoe ordered the 3rd B.C.S. to station itself twenty miles ahead of the Grand Fleet as a scouting force and to be in a position to rejoin the Battle Cruiser Fleet.

At 14.23 on the 31st the three ships were steering S.50°E at 14 knots when the *Indomitable* picked up a signal from the *Galatea* stating that she had enemy ships in sight. About an hour later the same ship heard that the Battle Cruiser Fleet had engaged the German battlecruisers. At 16.00 Hood led his ships away S.S.E. at full speed to reinforce Beatty, anticipating by five minutes the C. in C.'s order to do so.

At about 17.35 Hood heard some firing abaft his starboard beam and turned his force through eight points to investigate. Soon the *Chester*, from his own screen, appeared out of the mist surrounded by shell splashes. A few minutes later four German light cruisers came into view and found Hood's three battlecruisers bearing down on them. As the *Chester* escaped across her bows the *Invincible* opened fire at 17.55 followed by *Inflexible* and *Indomitable* at 18.00. The *Elbing* escaped but the *Pillau* and *Frankfurt* were heavily damaged and the *Wiesbaden* was reduced to a drifting wreck.

At this point the *Lion* appeared on the port bow, heading eastwards and heavily engaged with Hippers battlecruisers. Hood altered course to join her. Having reformed after a torpedo attack the 3rd B.C.S. came up from the East and were ordered by Beatty to take station ahead of him. At 18.26 they came round in a full semi-circle to starboard until they were heading S.E., in the van of the Battle Cruiser Fleet. They were almost immediately engaged by the German battlecruisers. The British ships had the advantage of the light and began to make excellent practice on the enemy scoring hits on the *Lutzow* and *Derfflinger* several times. But at 18.29 the mist between the *Invincible* and the enemy line momentarily cleared. Salvoes began to fall rapidly round the flagship and at 18.32 a shell hit Q turret, blowing off the roof. A few seconds later Q magazine exploded, closely followed by P. Wreckage was thrown 400 feet into the air and the British ship broke in two, each half sinking and coming to rest on the sea bed, leaving the bow and stern projecting above the water. There were six survivors including the gunnery officer. Admiral Hood, 61 officers, 965 men and 5 civilians were lost with the ship.

Despite being straddled several times the *Indomitable* and *Inflexible* received no damage during this action.

CONCLUSION

The battlecruiser has been condemned almost without exception, as a badly conceived and ill found warship type. The origin of this complete dismissal of an entire group of major warships stems, mainly, from the loss of three of their number at Jutland. This pointing, so it seemed, to the inadvisability of constructing vessels with too little armour and too much gunpower. The lack of armour has been, to most people (including myself), sufficient explanation for these losses and therefore condemnation of the battlecruiser concept. Such a sweeping statement, however, does not take account of all the evidence provided by a more detailed appraisal which reveals that, like most things connected with man's endeavours, the battlecruiser concept has so many variables that it is difficult to form a true picture of their value.

The *Invincible* class were conceived, designed and built as armoured cruisers and were so referred to until about 1912 when the term battlecruiser came into use. It was perhaps a dangerous change of designation, giving the impression that a completely new type of warship had been evolved. Although this was true from the design point of view it was not so as far as tactics were concerned for they were constructed for the same purpose as their predecessors. An examination of the *Invincible* class design reveals that they were in fact virtually armoured cruisers with a uniform armament of 12 in. guns. The displacement being dictated by the design requirements, and the installation of turbine machinery being part of the normal evolutionary process of machinery development. Nor was their large displacement unusual for many armoured and protected cruisers, almost as large as contemporary battleships, had already been constructed.

Fisher equipped the *Dreadnought* with turbine machinery and a uniform armament of 12 in. guns and thus revolutionised battleship construction overnight. She was a vessel well ahead of her time for Fisher had looked to the future and foreseen what was certain to happen to battleship design within a few years. He had thus placed the Royal Navy well ahead of her rivals by cutting out the intervening period of development, which had, in fact, already begun. The armoured cruiser was involved in the same development porcess and sensibly one can see that within a few years it would have followed the same path as the battleship – turbine machinery and a uniform armament. It can be safely assumed however that this armament would have consisted of 9.2 in. guns and not the 12 in. that were fitted in the *Invincibles.*

The argument put forward by Fisher for the all big gun armoured cruiser must have seemed very convincing and can briefly be summarised as follows:– They were capable of destroying any vessel fast enough to catch them and fast enough to escape any vessel capable of destroying them. There is a serious flaw in this argument however, for it assumes that an enemy does not possess similar vessels. Once Germany began the construction of battlecruisers the value of the *Invincibles* diminished considerably for it could be expected that in war time they would come into action against vessels of the same calibre. In these circumstances we can picture two vessels, both armed with heavy guns capable of penetrating each others armour and neither able to escape from the other. The terms of the engagement would be something like those for Russian Roulette. This is, however, an over simplification of the situation for Germany and Britain constructed their battlecruisers upon slightly different lines.

Indomitable in 1918, showing her final wartime appearance. Note the 36" searchlight at the rear end of the after shelter, the 4" A.A. gun abaft the fore-funnel and the searchlight towers abreast the main mast.▽

In the German ships a greater percentage of the weight was provided for armour and water tight subdivision, at the expense of speed and gunpower. This made them difficult to sink but it must be noted that German armour was not of the same quality as that of the British ships. They also, after the Dogger Bank action, had the advantage of flash tight magazines.

British battlecruisers carried guns of heavier calibre, which gave them greater range and hitting power, and more powerful machinery giving higher speed. Unlike the German designs armour and sub division came a poor third to these requirements.

The value of these designs can best be judged by the results of the Battle of Jutland, mainly in relation to the loss of the *Invincible, Queen Mary* and *Indefatigable,* which, as I have already stated, was the prime cuase of the loss of confidence in British battlecruiser design. The experience of the *Lion* gives a good idea of what probably occured aboard the three ships that were lost. The *Lion's* Q turret was hit and penetrated, by an 11 in. shell from the *Lutzow,* at the joint of the front plate and the roof. The shell exploded over the breech of one of the guns and killed or wounded the entire crew of the gunhouse. The breech of the gun was forced downward by the explosion and a shell, which was being loaded into the gun when the projectile struck, slid out of the open breech and knocked over some cordite charges in the well at the rear of the gun. These fell onto some burning rags and ignited. The resultant flash went down the turret trunk and, but for the fact that doors had been closed and the magazine flooded shortly after the turret had been hit, would certainly have detonated the magazine.

In the case of *Invincible, Queen Mary* and *Indefatigable* there was also a short delay after they had been hit before the magazines exploded and it may, reasonably, be assumed that similar events occured aboard these ships. Had any shells penetrated direct to the magazine the explosion would probably have been instantaneous.

Thus it can be seen that it was not lack of armour that caused these losses but the absence of magazine isolation and the instability of the cordite, which was supposed to burn and not flash. Had the British realised the danger sooner and fitted flash tight scuttles to their magazines none of these ships would have been lost. At the end of the day Beatty's battlecruiser force would have been complete and, although it may have been damaged with several turrets out of action, it would not have been in the same sorry state as the German battlecruisers which were saved by their excellent system of sub–division, their armour, magazine isolation and the fact that the battle came to an end before it had really begun. In these circumstances the heavier broadside of the British force could have demonstrated its full value and the post Jutland history of battlecruiser development may well have been different. The greater range of the British guns did not provide as much advantage as expected, gun control not being in an efficient enough state to secure hits to any appreciable extent at long distances. The advantage of speed possessed by the British ships proved of great tactical advantage and this was well demonstrated at the Falklands, Dogger Bank and Jutland.

One may see in the above an attempt to vindicate the battlecruiser policy. This however is not the intention, my purpose being to demonstrate that the British ships, which have been adversely compared with their German counterparts, were not as bad as they have been painted. It is a good rule that warships should be designed with at least sufficient armour to keep out shells of their own calibre. The battlecruisers, of both nations, suffered from weak deck protection and as battles were fought at much greater ranges during the war than anticipated, shells coming down at a very steep angle might well have penetrated a magazine direct. It would also have been quite easy, as was the case with the *Lion* at Dogger Bank, to damage the machinery. A ship with reduced or no motive power or no steering is of little use in the line of battle.

The battlecruiser was a hybrid, being neither cruiser nor battleship. The taxpayers' money could have been better spent on an

◁ *Another view of Indomitable in 1918. One of her 50′ steam boats is in the water alongside and her 40′ steam barge is being lowered by the main derrick. Note the aircraft on P & Q turrets.*

INDOMITABLE, 1918

1. A turret
2. Training scale
3. Carley raft
4. Foreward C.T.
5. Navigating bridge
6. Compass platform
7. Short range W.T. aerials
8. Range finder
9. Gun director
10. Fore top
11. 36" search light
12. Range clock
13. Signal lamp
14. 24" search light
15. Siren

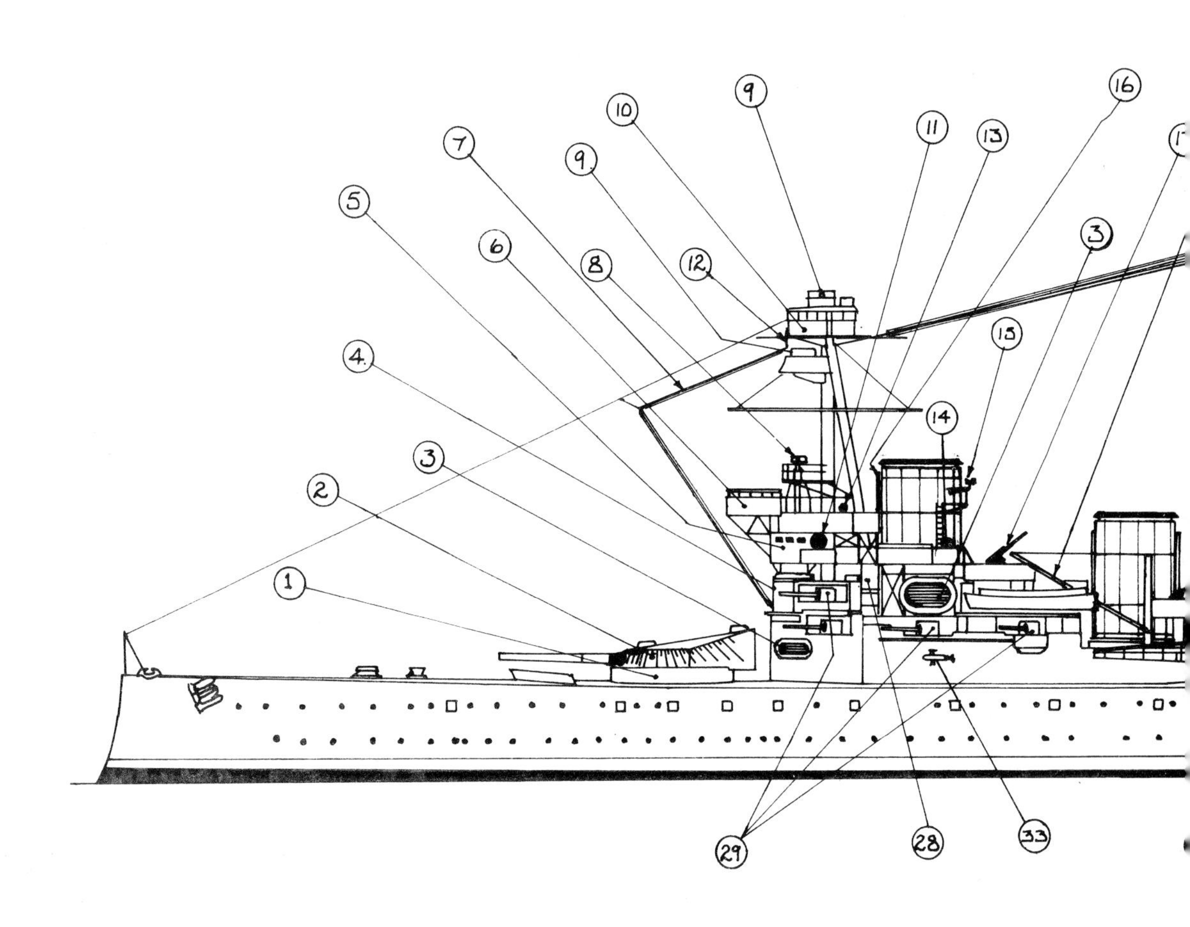

INDOMITABLE 1918

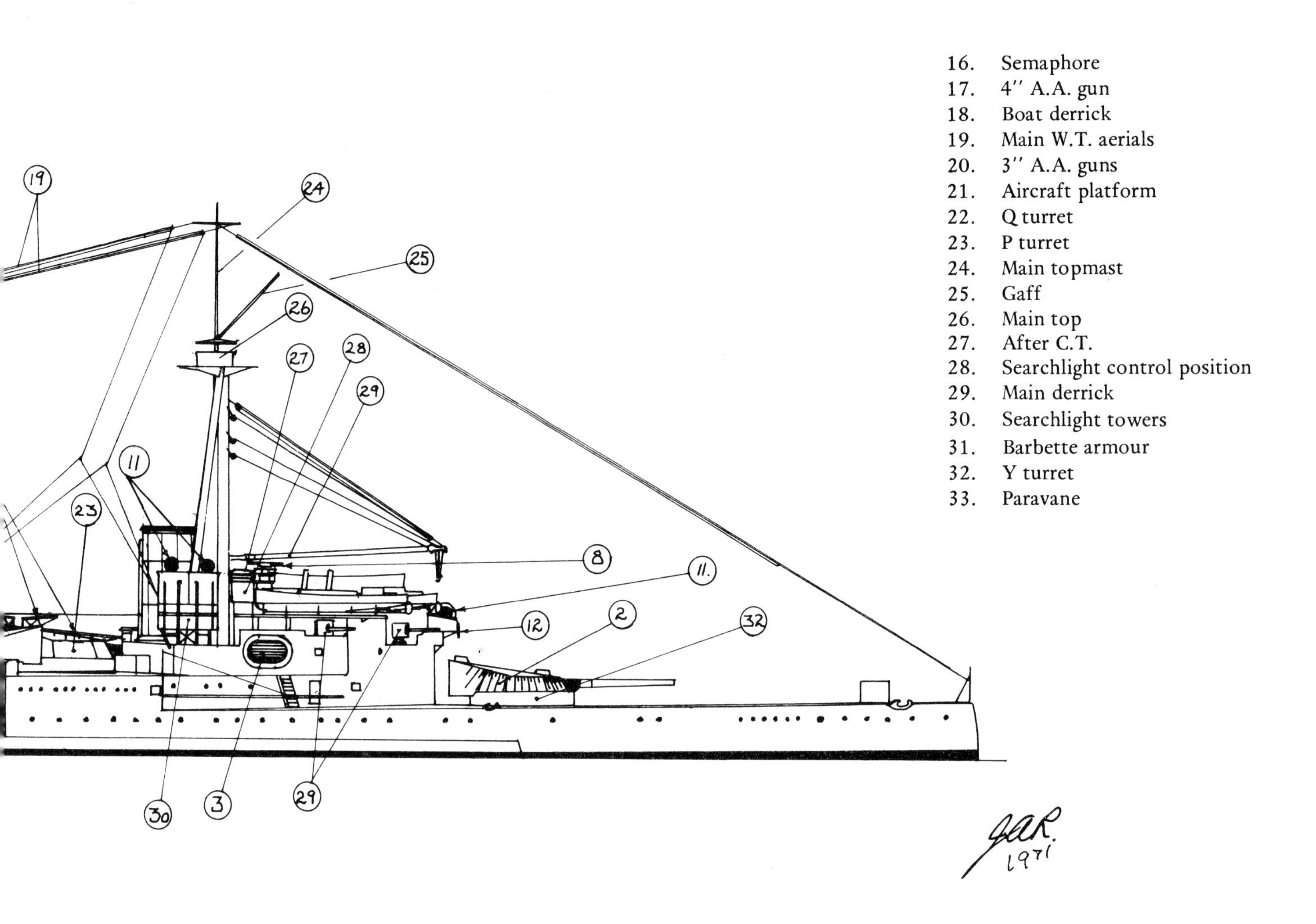

16. Semaphore
17. 4″ A.A. gun
18. Boat derrick
19. Main W.T. aerials
20. 3″ A.A. guns
21. Aircraft platform
22. Q turret
23. P turret
24. Main topmast
25. Gaff
26. Main top
27. After C.T.
28. Searchlight control position
29. Main derrick
30. Searchlight towers
31. Barbette armour
32. Y turret
33. Paravane

Invincible with say four 12 in. guns and much heavier armour or on the development of a fast battleship with slightly reduced armament, greater speed and armour on the same scale as a battleship. It must be realised, however, that this latter course would have resulted in a new, larger and much more expensive type of battleship which of necessity could be only built in small numbers. Any advantage gained by producing a revolutionary type of warship lasts only as long as it takes an enemy or potential enemy to build a ship of equal power. It is far better to take existing designs and make them as efficient as possible. The *Dreadnought* revolutionised battleship construction not because she was completely different from previous battleships but because she was much more efficient. It would have been better if Fisher had been content with producing the *Dreadnought* and a conventional armoured cruiser with a uniform armament of 9.2 in guns powered by turbine machinery.

Left: The 2nd Battle Cruiser Squadron at sea in 1918. The Inflexible and Australia taken from the Indomitable's fore top. Below: H.M.S. Indomitable, 1916. Note 3" A.A. gun abreast midships funnel and Carley rafts.